GENERAL PALAEONTOLOGY

pg, line, word, letter

GENERAL
PALAEONTOLOGY

A. Brouwer

Translated by
R. H. Kaye

THE UNIVERSITY OF CHICAGO PRESS

FIRST EDITION 1959

Algemene Paleontologie
W. de Haan N.V
Zinzendorflaan
Zeist
The Netherlands

FIRST ENGLISH EDITION 1967
Second Impression 1968

Library of Congress Catalog Card Number 67-18435

The University of Chicago Press, Chicago 60637
Oliver and Boyd, Ltd, Edinburgh & London

PREFACE

General palaeontology is not a new branch of the science of palaeontology, but it is a subject whose study has been greatly neglected. This becomes apparent as soon as the poverty of its literature is compared with the number of books on systematic palaeontology. Since Walther's *Allgemeine Paläontologie* appeared in 1927 there has not been a single textbook covering the whole field of general palaeontology, and the literature of most special aspects of the subject is also sparse. The revival of sedimentary geology has, however, stimulated interest in general palaeontology.

Encouraged by this development, since 1954 I have given lectures on general palaeontology to undergraduate students in geology. This book is one of the fruits of those lectures. It is, therefore, intended primarily for students, but I hope that others will also find it useful.

In the present state of general palaeontology it is not possible to give an all-embracing, systematic treatment of the whole field, because there are still too many gaps in our knowledge. This book will have fulfilled its purpose if it encourages further research into general palaeontological problems.

A. BROUWER

CONTENTS

CHAPTER 1

LIFE AND DEATH

1. *Introduction*

It is not known for how long life has existed on the Earth. It can, however, be stated that the present pattern of animal life, in which the insects are the group with the greatest number of species and the mammals are usually considered as the most highly evolved of living creatures, has existed only for a very short time. The most striking characteristic of life on Earth is the continual variation of the forms in which it finds expression.

The number of individuals which has populated the Earth since life began is beyond estimation. Most of them have disappeared without trace but a few have left behind evidence of their existence in the form of fossils—the recognisable remains of living creatures from the geological past. " Recognisable " is a necessary qualification since sedimentary deposits such as coal seams consist wholly or partly of the remains of organisms, but are not called fossils as the component individuals are no longer recognisable as such.

What exactly is to be understood by " the geological past " is partly a question of taste. In such countries as the Netherlands, where important geographical changes have occurred in the last few thousand years, there is a tendency to think of the geological past as continuing into more recent times than in areas where the geographical pattern has remained virtually unaltered over a longer period.

Palaeontology is the science concerned with the study of fossils. It would be difficult to discuss fossils if they had no names and no place in a natural system. The description, naming and classification of fossils is the particular function of *systematic palaeontology*, where the same rules apply as in the nomenclature and classification of recent organisms—a good natural system should embrace both recent and fossil organisms. Systematic palaeontology is therefore closely connected with systematic botany and zoology, and a knowledge of recent forms is a necessary condition for the successful study of fossils, just as a knowledge of fossils is necessary for a complete understanding of the recent flora and fauna. The complementary nature of the two studies is reflected in the term "neontology" which is used to denote the study of recent organisms.

Description, identification and classification, however, are only the first stages in the study of fossils. A fossil is the remains of an organism which had a particular place in geological history, in both time and space; in time because life on Earth is subject to continual change, and in space because a living organism is attached to a particular environment and, in a wider context, to the whole geographical pattern of its period. Time and space are therefore reflected in the occurrence and distribution of fossils in sediments: the analysis of a sedimentary deposit is only complete when attention has been paid equally to its organic components (the fossils) and to its inorganic components (the rock particles).

General palaeontology embraces all these aspects of the science. It includes stratigraphic palaeontology which is concerned with the vertical distribution of fossils, palaeoecology which is the study of fossils in relation to their environment, and palaeobiogeography, the study of the geographical distribution of fossils.

From whatever point of view they are studied, it should always be remembered that fossils are the remains of living creatures. Therefore it is clear that before discussing the subjects mentioned above in greater detail, certain aspects of palaeontology which are directly relevant to the transition from life to death must be considered.

2. *Fossils as the remains of living creatures*

It should constantly be borne in mind in all subsequent discussions of fossils that they are the remains of living creatures which had all the characteristic properties of life—metabolism, growth, reproduction and in most cases movement.

Metabolism partly consists of the release of energy, because potential energy is converted into kinetic energy:

$$\text{carbohydrates} + \text{oxygen} \longrightarrow \text{carbon dioxide} + \text{water} + \text{energy}$$

In its simplest form this process, the respiratory process in animals, can be represented by the formula:

$$C_6H_{12}O_6 + 6O_2 \rightarrow 6CO_2 + 6H_2O + 674,000 \text{ cal}$$

The oxygen is derived from the environment and the carbohydrates from food, and thus fuel is supplied. In animals, and also in all non-green plants, food is comprised of organic materials and mineral salts. The organic part is derived from other living creatures, or at least from their remains. Only green plants are able, by means of chlorophyll, to utilise sunlight to build organic materials from CO_2 and H_2O:

carbon dioxide + water + energy → starch + oxygen

The process of assimilation of carbon dioxide by photosynthesis is the exact reverse of respiration. These two processes are complementary and essential for the maintenance of the natural economy.

Because animals are not able to form organic materials out of inorganic materials it follows that they must have appeared after the green plants in geological history. Food not only provides the necessary fuel for the vital physiological functions, but also the materials which are needed for growth and where necessary the materials from which to build reserves. In certain circumstances growth may be inhibited and this can lead to the emergence of dwarf specimens. In particular environments the entire fauna may acquire this character; later it will be seen that this is important for an explanation of the environment of some fossil dwarf faunas.

Reproduction is of the greatest importance from the palaeontological point of view. The infinitesimal differences between one generation and the next which arise during reproduction are ultimately responsible for that long evolution which life has displayed in the history of the Earth (see Chapter 5).

Although in most plants and animals the elementary physiological functions proceed according to a single basic pattern, this is realised in very different ways in different groups. This becomes clear when the respiratory mechanisms of various groups of invertebrates are compared. Even within a single group the differences may still be considerable: the same respiratory pattern, for example, has been realised in entirely different ways in the mammals and in the fishes. That the environment need not always be a determining factor can be seen from a comparison of fish with aquatic mammals.

Feeding and reproduction also show that the same principle may be effected in entirely different ways in different groups.

Usually the palaeontologist has only the hard parts of former organisms at his disposal: external shells, external or internal skeletal elements. The question arises, therefore, whether such parts provide an adequate basis for interpreting the mode of life of an organism. To do this an accurate comparison with recent organisms is indispensable. Even then many doubtful points will remain, especially with groups of organisms that have no close relations among recent floras or faunas. Nevertheless, these hard parts often provide data on the mode of life of the creatures in question. A few examples will illustrate this.

Some species of lamellibranchs live in the sea-bed. The mechanical demands made on the shells of these species are much smaller than those made on the shells of species inhabiting the surf zone. In view of this, species which spend their lives buried in the sea-bed generally have much thinner shells.

Moreover, when their shells are in a closed position an opening remains between the two valves through which the siphon is extruded. In practically all other lamellibranchs the valves fit tightly together when the shell is closed. Here is one example where a

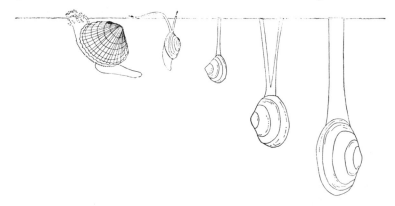

Fig. 1. Some recent examples of burrowing lamellibranchs. From left to right: *Cardium, Tellina, Macoma, Scrobicularia* and *Mya.*
After Young and Thamdrup.

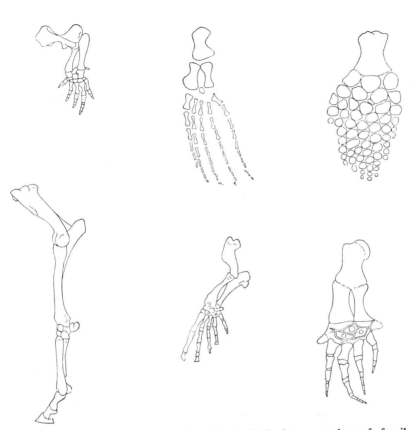

Fig. 2. Skeletal structure of the left forelimb in a number of fossil reptiles (upper row) and mammals (lower row). Reptiles, from left to right: *Ophiacodon* (a primitive reptile), *Tylosaurus* and *Ichthyosaurus* (two marine reptiles). Mammals, from left to right: *Equus, Arctocephalus* (Pinnipedia), *Balaena* (Cetacea). After Williston, Romer, Gregory, Van Beneden and Gervais.

shell, or even a single valve, provides important information (Fig. 1).

The limbs of mammals furnish quite a different kind of example of the connection between hard parts and mode of life. In nearly all mammals limbs are organs of propulsion. There are, however, appreciable differences according to environment (Fig. 2). The limbs of seals and other pinnipeds are an extreme case; these are meant not for movement on land but for swimming. An even greater divergence may be observed in the whales. Here the tail has acquired the function of an organ of propulsion; the forelimbs serve as a means of steering, while in recent whales the rear limbs have disappeared completely. This development has had its effect on the pelvis which has been drastically reduced, almost to vanishing point. Comparable differences also exist among the reptiles. The vertebral columns of the whales also reflect the transference of the propulsive function to the tail. A powerful tail requires suitable points of attachment for the tail muscles, and consequently the whales in contrast to other mammals have their largest vertebrae in the tail region of the vertebral column.

The cervical region of the vertebral column of the whales also shows the influence on this group of special adaptation to an aquatic mode of life (Fig. 3). Like other mammals whales have seven cervical vertebrae. There is, however, scarcely any external indication of a neck; the cervical vertebrae are no more than shallow disks which are sometimes partially fused together. This naturally results in a reduced mobility of the head in relation to the body, so that there is a close approximation to a rigid torpedo-like form.

Whales, therefore, are a good example of a group whose skeletons are constructed according to a certain pattern, common to all mammals, but which show special variations of this pattern as a result of adaptation to an aquatic mode of life. Mammals and other vertebrates could furnish many other instances of the connection between mode of life and skeletal structure. That this kind of connection should exist is hardly surprising; the skeleton of a vertebrate is closely connected, literally, with the soft parts via the muscles.

This connection is by no means so apparent in the invertebrates, and it has received much less attention. A single example may illustrate how a new insight into the mode of life of extinct animals can be gained by a closer analysis of their hard parts. Nearly every geologist knows from his own experience how much variation ammonite shells display in such easily perceptible properties as the number of whorls, the width of these whorls and relative length of the body-chamber. These are generally accepted as useful diagnostic characters for purposes of identification. However, Trueman (1941) tried to answer the question of what consequences

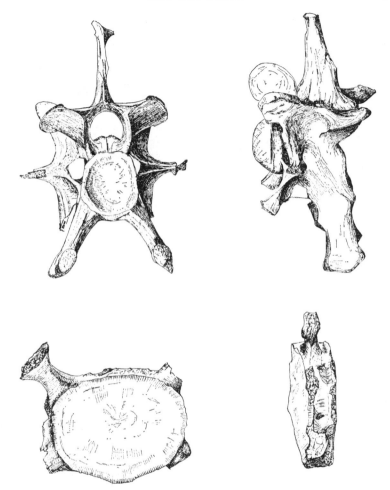

Fig. 3. Rear and left side elevation of two fossil cervical vertebrae. *Above* a typical land mammal. *Cervus elaphus* (× 2/5), *below* a marine mammal, *Balaenoptera* (× 1/4). After specimens from the Rijksmuseum van Geologie en Mineralogie, Leiden.

would such variations have had on the mode of life of the ammonites. Two points are of importance here: (*i*) the density of the complete animal and (*ii*) the attitude of the shell.

In order to determine the density of the animal it is necessary to know the specific gravity of the body, the volume ratio of the air-chambers to the body-chamber, the ratio of the volume of the shell material to the total volume, and the density of the shell material. Naturally the first of these cannot be determined for fossils. Trueman therefore assumed that the relation between the weight of the body and the volume of the body-chamber was the same in ammonites as in the recent *Nautilus*, in which case the density for a completely filled body-chamber would be 1·13. The ratio of the volume of the shell material to the total volume and the volume ratio of air-chambers to body-chamber can be determined by sectional measurements. The density of the shell material presents another difficulty, since it is not known whether this was calcite (d. 2·72) or aragonite (d. 2·94). Trueman based his calculations on aragonite. A simple calculation will show that when the volume ratio of air-chambers to body-chamber is 1 : 3, and the volume of the shell material is 1/16 of the total volume, the density of the complete ammonite must have been exactly equal to that of sea water.

It is certainly remarkable how many ammonites have a ratio of air-chambers to body-chamber lying just a little below 1 : 3, while the volume of the shell material usually amounts to 1/10 to 1/15 of the total volume. Consequently Trueman was inclined to assume that most ammonites had approximately the same density as sea water—they were able to float in the water and they could also rise or sink by making small movements of the body in relation to the shell. In ammonites with a volume ratio of air-chambers to body-chamber rather less favourable than 1 : 3, the shell may often be observed to be especially thin, thereby compensating for the greater weight of the body.

If there is a further increase in the relative size of the body-chamber, a critical limit is ultimately reached beyond which equilibrium is no longer feasible. If the shell were completely weightless, this limit would occur at a ratio of 1 : 7·7. The actual limit must lie rather higher than this. Even smaller ratios occur, however, and it is generally assumed that such species were unable to float in the water and, therefore, had a benthonic mode of life.

A second point which Trueman considered was the attitude of the ammonites during life. This, of course, determines the direction of the shell opening. When suspended at rest in the water, the attitude of the shell is determined by the relative positions of the centre of gravity of the whole animal and of the centre of buoyancy of water displaced. The attitude of the shell will always be such that the centre of gravity lies below the centre of buoyancy. The greater the distance between the two points the greater the stability. The position of the centre of gravity is fixed by the position of the centres of gravity of the shell and of the body; the centre of gravity of the whole animal lies on the line joining these two points, and is closer to the centre of gravity of the body than to that of the shell. The weight of the shell, however, is so insignificant compared with the weight of the body that, for the sake of simplicity, Trueman took the centre of gravity of the body as being the centre of gravity of the whole animal. Determining the centre of gravity of the shell is tedious, and not rewarded by the greater accuracy attained. This was verified using a recent *Nautilus*.

Now it can easily be seen that the centre of gravity and the centre of buoyancy will be close together in an ammonite where the body-chamber occupies an entire whorl of the shell. The attitude of the shell would have been less stable so that it is quite conceivable that in such cases the animals could vary the attitude of their shells, and consequently the direction of the shell opening, by small movements of the body in relation to the body-chamber—in other words by retracting or extruding the body.

In ammonites with a body-chamber the size of a half whorl, the distance between the centre of gravity and the centre of buoyancy was much greater and the attitude of the animal much more stable in consequence. The shell opening of such ammonites would have been directed more or less vertically upwards (Fig. 4).

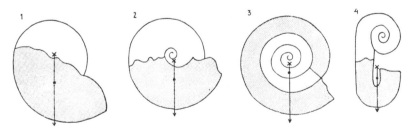

Fig. 4. Extent of the body-chamber (shaded), position of the centre of buoyancy (cross) and of the centre of gravity (dot) in the recent *Nautilus* (1) and in three ammonites, *Sigaloceras* (2), *Dactylioceras* (3) and *Macroscaphites* (4). After Trueman from Basse.

It is apparent then that the length of the body-chamber, expressed in whorls, is an important factor for the attitude of the shell and the stability of the animal during its life. The shell of the normal ammonite type may be thought of as a cone that has been coiled and the length of the body-chamber can then be expressed in relation to the height of this cone. In many ammonites the body-chamber appears to form approximately 1/3 of the cone, the base of the cone representing the shell opening. How large the extent of the body-chamber will be, expressed in number of whorls, then depends on the form of the cone (Fig. 5): the smaller the angle at the apex, the greater the number of whorls when the cone is coiled. Given ammonites with equal relative measurements of the body-chamber to the height of the cone, the extent of the body-chamber expressed in whorls becomes greater as the apsidal angle becomes smaller. Minimum stability occurs when the body-chamber occupies one whorl. If the body-chamber is greater than one whorl, then the stability increases again until one and a half whorls are occupied.

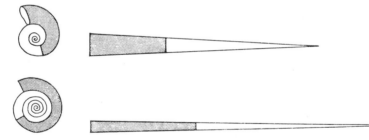

Fig. 5.   Relation between absolute and relative length of the body-chamber in ammonites as a function of the spiral angle. After Trueman.

The size of the vertical angle is also reflected in the spiral angle of the coiled ammonite shell. The smaller the vertical angle, the nearer the spiral angle approaches to 90°. In practice the spiral angle lies approximately between 80° and 87°.

Trueman's investigations clearly demonstrate the way in which a closer examination of generally known facts can lead to a better understanding of fossils as living animals. Much remains to be done in this field, particularly with invertebrates.

3. *Death*

The death of an organism may be due to a variety of causes. Some of these, such as senescence, may be found in the organism itself, others are external and include such factors as enemies, changes in the environment or entry of the organism into an unsuitable environment.

Fossils sometimes give indications of the cause of death. In fossil vertebrates morbid growths of bone tissue caused by some pathological and possibly fatal condition are occasionally observed.

External causes of death can usually be reconstructed with greater certainty. Numerous examples are known, particularly of fossil vertebrates, where the fossilised remains of other animals or plants, which evidently served as food, were found in the gastric region. One organism may cause the death of another without there necessarily being a predator-prey relationship between them; it may be the result of ecological hostility. The smothering of banks of *Cardium edule* by a massive overgrowth of *Mytilus edulis* is an example of this. Ecological competition is undoubtedly a cause of death which occurs frequently in nature but is difficult to prove in fossils. The evidence is usually only clear in the case of sessile animals, as in the example mentioned above, where in favourable circumstances victors and vanquished are preserved together *in situ*. Even in these cases the possible effect of small changes in the environment should be taken into account.

From the geological point of view, fossils of organisms which met their death through changes in the environment are of particular importance because they provide not only a palaeontological document but also data for the reconstruction of the environment itself, a point which is discussed in more detail in Chapter 2. The attitude of the organism can be passive or active. In the first case the environment itself changes, in the second the organism changes its environment. The results of these two possibilities must be considered separately.

The effect of a change in environment on a particular organism is dependent on: (*i*) the extent to which the environment changes, (*ii*) the speed at which the environment changes, (*iii*) the possibility of the organism living in the new environment, and (*iv*) the possibility of the organism leaving the changed environment.

The third factor can be of great importance in palaeoecological studies. Although a particular species may be able to live in the new environment, there may be an associated increase or decrease in the number of individuals, possibly resulting from either the appearance or disappearance of ecological competitors. This factor need not be taken into account in an examination of causes of death. The first factor is also relevant to palaeoecological studies; the greater the environmental changes, the greater the likelihood of their having serious consequences. At this stage, however, only changes in environment which actually lead to the death of organisms or species need be discussed. In this connection the speed at which these changes occur and the possibility of the inhabitants evacuating to another environment are of particular importance. Plants and animals with a sessile mode of life do not have this possibility of evacuation and are therefore doomed if the new environment proves unsuitable. The root-like organs of *Lepidodendron*, the so-called *Stigmaria* roots of the Upper Carboniferous, are an example of trees that were killed by environmental change and fossilised *in situ* (Fig. 6).

Coral reefs may die either because the sea level rises faster than their vertical growth, or because the reef reaches the surface of

Fig. 6.   Stumps of Carboniferous trees fossilised *in situ* (*Lepidodendron*). After Young and Glen, from Potonié.

the water. In the first case, the whole reef dies because the depth of the water ultimately becomes greater than that at which the reef-builders can live. In the second case, vertical growth is replaced by outward horizontal growth and the central section of the reef dies. From the point of view of the organism, both of these are instances of environmental change.

Finally, the death of a non-sessile animal can occur through displacement from a suitable to an unsuitable environment. Many instances, both fossil and recent, are known of this. Undoubtedly the best examples come from the fauna of the Solnhofen limestone (Tithonian, Upper Jurassic) in the region of the Altmühl, a left tributary of the Danube in Bavaria. The position of certain fossils at the ends of trails which the animals must have made in the last moments of their lives, indicates that this is where death occurred (Fig. 7). This also applies to some fossils in which evidence of a death struggle may be discerned. Walther, and later Abel, have shown that the animals concerned in most of these instances did not normally inhabit the limestone lagoon and died as a result of entering this special environment.

For most animals death means the beginning of a period of passive transport. Creatures which fly usually fall to the ground, and those which are aquatic mostly sink to the bottom. The carcases of whales are exempted from the law of gravity by the development of gases in their bodies which cause them to float.

Consequently Schäfer (1955) believed that most dead whales must be washed ashore eventually. This may explain concentrations of fossil whales, as in the Miocene of Antwerp. Something of this type may also apply to other groups of animals. It is conceivable that the empty shells of the nautiloids and ammonites would float, although it is questionable whether such shells are really capable of sailing, as it were, across whole oceans. But even for the remains of animals which reach the ground or the sea-bed soon after death, or who died there, this does not necessarily mean final rest.

Fig. 7. *Limulus walchi* Desm., fossilised at the end of its trail (Upper Jurassic, Eichstätt). After data from Walther and Abel.

Running water, wind and other animals can cause further transport. The roots of plants usually remain in the ground, but trunks and stalks, foliage and flowers may be carried considerable distances.

It is obvious therefore that the place where the remains of a dead organism finally come to rest and become buried in sediment does not generally correspond with the place where death occurred. It has already been shown that the latter does not necessarily coincide with the normal habitat of the organism. Distinction must therefore be made between the normal habitat, the place where the organism died, and the place where its remains were eventually enclosed in sediment. These three places may coincide (Fig. 8, aa), in which case fossilised remains, if present, are referred to as *autochthonous fossils.* Burrowing lamellibranchs can die and be fossilised in the sediment in the attitude they had when alive. This is also the case with corals which are fossilised *in situ* with the whole reef. These are particularly well-defined examples of autochthonous fossils. The places in which an organism lived, died and became buried, however, may not coincide, in which case the term *allochthonous fossil* is used (Fig. 8, bb).

As will appear from Fig. 8 there are two other possibilities between these two extremes, whereby two of the three events (life, death and enclosure in the sediment) may occur at the same place. An organism may die in its normal environment, be subsequently transported and enclosed in the sediment elsewhere (Fig. 8, ab); or it may die at a place outside its normal environment and become buried there (Fig. 8, ba). Examples of the latter type are found in the fossilised animals which left trails or evidence of a death-

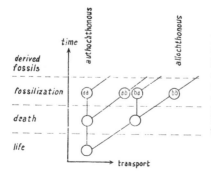

Fig. 8. Diagram showing autochthony and allochthony in fossils. Each circle represents a particular event (life, death, etc.) at a particular place. A vertical connection between two circles means that no transport occurred between the two events; a connection with a horizontal component means that transport did occur.

struggle in the Solnhofen limestone. The term *autochthonous-alloch-thonous fossil* is employed to indicate both of these intermediate possibilities, but it is clear that these are really allochthonous fossils from the ecological point of view, as the remains are found at a place outside the normal environment of the organism. Apart from such rare finds, where trails and similar evidence remain, in practice it is seldom possible to determine where the organism died, and consequently the distinction between the possibilities (ab), (ba) and (bb) is largely theoretical. What is essential, however, is to decide whether a fossil is autochthonous or allochthonous. This point will be returned to in the discussion of ecological analysis in Chapter 2.

The term *biostratonomy* embraces all the processes which occur between death, or between the onset of the death-struggle, and the final enclosure of organic remains in the sediment. These biostrato-nomical events precede actual fossilisation and a thorough under-standing of them is often important for an interpretation of the processes of fossilisation. Biostratonomical processes are best studied in recent organisms and this forms one aspect of the somewhat strangely named science of *actuopalaeontology*.

4. *Fossilisation*

Mechanical, chemical and biological attack quickly destroy the remains of most organisms. Only if the remains are removed from these destructive agents shortly after death is there a chance of anything being preserved as a fossil. Enclosure within some sort of medium, usually a sediment, offers the best chances of this taking place. The term fossilisation includes all the processes which occur between the covering of organic remains by a sediment, or any other comparable medium, and the formation of a fossil. The end product of the process is a fossil—an organic remain which has acquired a certain measure of physico-chemical stability with regard to its environment.

From this it follows that the likelihood of an organism becoming a fossil depends on: (*i*) the organism itself and (*ii*) the environ-ment where the organism ultimately comes to rest after death. The composition of the organism is implied in (*i*). Animals or plants which possess hard parts—shell, skeleton or wood—stand a better chance of surviving the critical period between death and enclosure in a sediment than those which do not. The so-called soft parts, composed of carbohydrates and proteins, usually disappear rapidly after death, especially if they have a high water content. It is well known, for example, that nothing remains of jellyfish a short time after death. In contrast the shells of molluscs or the skeletal elements of mammals resist mechanical, chemical or biological attack for a considerable time. Consequently the palaeontological record of species or groups with hard parts is much richer than that of those without them. In a comparatively young group, such as the mammals, approximately the same number of fossil as recent species is known, while in the insects, a much older group, the number of fossil species known amounts to only a fraction of the recent species.

The influence of environment (*ii*) means that organisms living in surroundings where continual sedimentation occurs, or arriving there after death, have the best chance of fossilisation. The sea-bed in general forms an area of sedimentation, whereas on land, sedimentation is restricted to certain specialised environments, usually small in extent and isolated in situation—flood-plains, lakes, driftsands, etc. Consequently the palaeontological record of marine organisms is more complete than that of non-marine ones. Nevertheless the extent of present knowledge of, for example, land mammals and reptiles is surprising and obviously this is due to their possession of hard parts.

A fossil rarely consists of the same substances as the equivalent parts of the living organism. Chemical changes almost invariably occur which produce greater stability. In addition to the organic materials of which soft parts are comprised (carbohydrates and proteins), the following substances occur in the composition of living creatures:

(*i*) calcite (hexagonal-rhombic modification of $CaCO_3$) is found in some flagellates, most foraminifera, some sponges, stromatoporoids, many extinct corals, most bryozoans, most brachiopods, some molluscs, some crustaceans and all echinoderms.

(*ii*) aragonite (orthorhombic modification of $CaCO_3$) is found in most scleractinian corals and in molluscs.

(*iii*) calcium phosphate is found in conularids, most inarticulate brachiopods, many arthropods and in vertebrates.

(*iv*) silica (opal, $SiO_2.nH_2O$) is found in some flagellates, most radiolaria and many sponges.

(*v*) combination of organic compounds, possibly with the addition of other constituents, is found in insects, certain arthropods and graptolites in the form of chitin, and in plants—cuticles, spores and pollen-grains.

These various substances are not equally stable. Calcite, for example, is a more stable modification of calcium carbonate than aragonite and consequently occurs more frequently in fossils. Few fossils consist of their original substances because the final composition of the material of which they are comprised is dependent on the physico-chemical properties of the sediment. After enclosure in a sediment, most parts of organisms which are preserved as fossils undergo chemical change and acquire greater stability with regard to the surrounding medium. Little attention has so far been paid to these processes. Many detailed palaeontological descriptions make no mention at all of the conditions under which fossilisation has taken place. It may be assumed, however, that similar processes are involved in the formation of concretions in sediments, a subject about which just as little is known.

Three compounds predominate in fossils, namely silica (chalcedony and quartz), calcium carbonate (mainly calcite) and calcium phosphate. Silica and calcite form the majority of invertebrate fossils. Calcium phosphate occurs mostly in the vertebrates, either by itself or impregnated with other substances.

After these three substances, which together account for more than 90 per cent of all fossils, come pyrite and carbon. Pyritisation occurs particularly under anaerobic conditions, in which free sulphur originating in decomposing soft parts combines with iron to form FeS_2. Pyritised fossils therefore occur mainly in dark, clayey sediments containing a certain amount of organic matter. Carbonisation is particularly prevalent in fossil plants where concentration of carbon eventually takes place. This process is comparable to the formation of coal.

Finally, numerous other substances are encountered in fossils. Their occurrence is dependent on the physico-chemical circumstances prevailing in the sediment after the enclosure of organic remains and on the substances available in the system. Common metals may be replaced by rare ones if these are present—possibly as the result of magmatic activity. Thus in addition to calcium carbonate, other carbonates are encountered as substances in fossils: zinc carbonate is found in Triassic lamellibranchs from Siberia and copper carbonate in plants from Germanic facies of the Trias. Phosphates of zinc and lead occur in vertebrates of the South African Cainozoic. Similarly, less common metals occur as sulphides and oxides. Among the latter iron oxide sometimes occurs as an oxidisation product from pyrite. Sulphates, of calcium, barium, strontium and lead, and silicates, particularly of iron and zinc, are also found in fossils. Chlorides and fluorides are very rare because of their solubility. Lastly, uncombined copper and silver should be included in this list of rare substances.

Theoretically, of course, there are any number of substances of which fossils, through conversion of their original material, could conceivably exist, but it is clear that in the great majority of cases a stable mixture of the most common substances is obtained. These are silica, calcium carbonate, calcium phosphate, iron sulphide and a number of organic compounds with a high carbon content. All other possibilities must be regarded as rarities and many of the instances quoted are unique.

Consideration of the component materials of fossils must be followed by study of their form. Fossilisation occurs in some sort of medium, usually a sediment. The organism, or the hard parts remaining after death, rests first on and later in the sediment. It may be preserved by remaining there for a long time and eventually appearing unchanged as a fossil. This, however, does not represent true fossilisation. Examples of this type of preservation, known as *subfossils*, occur frequently in Holocene deposits and may also be encountered in older deposits.

Usually, however, chemical changes, caused primarily by substances dissolved in percolating water, eventually occur in the sediment. Such changes influence not only the sediment (diagenesis), but also the organic remains which it contains. This can result in (*i*) solution, (*ii*) impregnation or (*iii*) replacement of the organic matter. In the case of (*i*), providing the sediment has become sufficiently hardened diagenetically, a cavity may be left in it which corresponds with the organic remains originally present. A cavity of this type may later be refilled either by natural agency (natural replica) or artificially with a plastic material (artificial replica). Such natural or artificial casts reveal the original form but not the structure of the organic material.

Impregnation (*ii*) is particularly likely to occur in porous substances, such as the skeletal elements of vertebrates, and produces well-preserved fossils.

Replacement (*iii*) of the original organic matter by another substance, usually calcium carbonate or silica, may take place very gradually so that fossils are produced in which not only their original form but also their original structure is preserved.

In each of these three cases it is possible for the sediment to show an external impression of the fossil.

In animals whose soft parts are enclosed by a shell (brachiopods, most molluscs) there are other modes of fossilisation. The internal cavity may be filled with sediment. This can become diagenetically hardened and be preserved, forming a cast of the internal cavity (internal mould). An internal mould is equally possible if the internal cavity is later filled with some material other than sediment. In either of these cases the shell, whether or not it is impregnated or completely converted, may be preserved. The shell, however, is not necessarily preserved—it may be dissolved away leaving only an internal mould, possibly with an external impression. If the internal mould is sufficiently connected with the surrounding sediment, then it is still possible for the cavity formed to be subsequently filled so that a combination of internal mould, and pseudomorph and external impression can also occur.

If the internal cavity does not become filled with sediment and the shell disappears, then a hollow is left in the sediment corresponding with the place occupied by the shell and the internal cavity together. If the sediment becomes sufficiently hardened, this space may be preserved, subsequently becoming filled with secondary material. The result is then a special type of pseudomorph.

Fig. 9 gives a survey in diagram form of the various ways in which a fossil record of an organism with an internal cavity, in this case a lamellibranch, may be preserved. It is obvious that a particular end-product may be the result of various developments, and it is often difficult or impossible to determine which of them has actually been responsible for a given fossil. Neverthe-

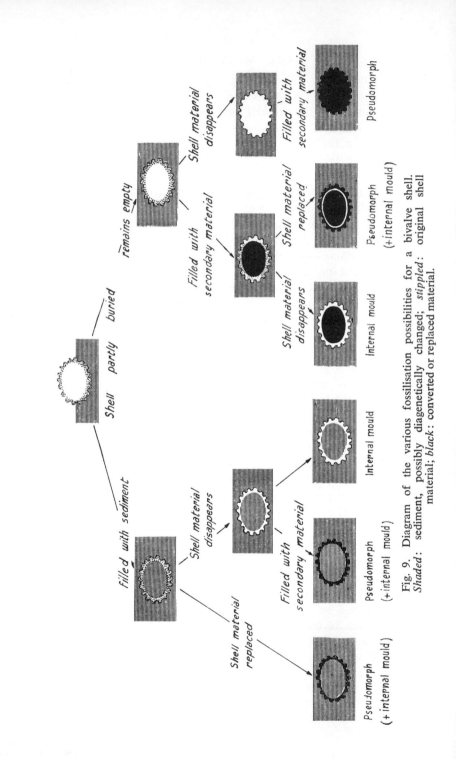

Fig. 9. Diagram of the various fossilisation possibilities for a bivalve shell. *Shaded*: sediment, possibly diagenetically changed; *stippled*: original shell material; *black*: converted or replaced material.

less, the circumstances of a particular organism before, at the time of, and after its death can often be reconstructed from a study of its history of fossilisation and an examination of the diagenesis of the sediment which should accompany it. These are points that ought not to be overlooked in palaeoecological analysis.

Internal moulds, therefore, occur where there has been an internal cavity originally containing soft parts, especially in brachiopods, in coelenterates, some arthropods and in molluscs—though not, of course, in dibranchiate molluscs which have an internal " shell ". Naturally the skeletal elements of vertebrates do not normally produce internal moulds, although a few rare instances of natural casts of the cranial cavity are known which could be

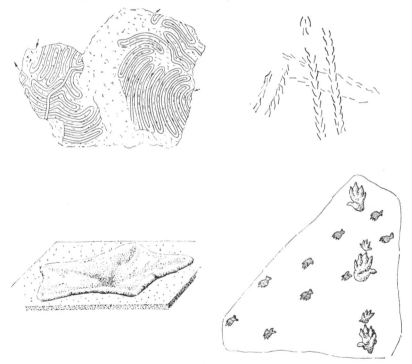

Fig. 10.   Examples of fossil tracks. *Top left*: *Helminthoida labyrinthica* from the Eocene Flysch, probably the track of a gastropod. *Top right*: from the Lower Permian, probably an insect track. *Bottom left*: *Asteriacites quinquefolius,* probably impression of a starfish. *Bottom right*: track, probably of *Chirotherium,* crossed by that of a much smaller unidentified animal, Triassic, Scotland. After Richter, Abel and Seilacher.

regarded as partial internal moulds of the skull. It is possible, however, that these represent a special manner of fossilisation of the soft parts themselves. For practical purposes this amounts to the same thing, although there is a great difference in the way in which the fossils have been produced.

The value of internal moulds from a systematic point of view differs greatly in various groups. The internal moulds of gastropods usually display very few characteristics of diagnostic value, as ornamentation of their shells is produced by a thickening of the shell material, of which the internal mould shows no trace. On the other hand, the ornamentation of ammonite and nautiloid shells is the result of folding of the shell material; and the internal mould which is a negative of the shell shows this. Moreover internal moulds of ammonites and nautiloids usually show the suture lines, an important diagnostic feature, and this makes internal moulds of both groups useful fossils.

Besides the fossils so far discussed, all of which constitute a more or less complete and essential relic of the organism itself, others are encountered which are not part of an organism as such. Amongst these are classed fossilised faeces, spores and other traces. Although different in their origin, these have one point in common —it is often impossible to determine from which of the known fossil species they came (Fig. 10).

5. *The reconstruction of fossil animals and plants*

Only in exceptional cases are the fossils of animals or plants so complete that their outward aspect during life can be visualised without considerable effort of the imagination. Fossilised remains usually represent no more than a part of an organism, so that much amplification is necessary before a complete picture can be obtained. No special problems are presented where animals with an external skeleton are concerned, particularly if they have comparable relatives among recent fauna. This is true for foraminifera, ostracods and other crustaceans, brachiopods and some of the molluscs, etc. Admittedly many details of the anatomy of their soft parts are lacking, but there is no reason to suppose that fossil brachiopods and lamellibranchs differed essentially in these aspects from recent representatives of the same group. The inner surfaces of shell-valves, which give some indication of what the soft parts are like, support this assumption. Only the colour of fossil species must remain hypothetical. Colour is a characteristic of living creatures and little remains of it after fossilisation.

Matters are quite different in animals with internal skeletons, particularly the vertebrates, where a clear distinction should be made between reconstruction of the skeleton of an animal and reconstruction of its external appearance. In the first place, many vertebrate skeletons are found incomplete. A fairly reliable result can sometimes be obtained by building a composite skeleton with elements from a number of examples of the same species, but uncertainties remain, even in this type of reconstruction, because many skeletal components, especially of the larger fossil vertebrates, have never been found. Even if all the parts of the skeleton of an individual may be accounted for, reconstruction is still difficult because the bones have usually become separated and their inter-relationship is not always immediately apparent. A consideration of anatomical function is often helpful.

If a comparison is made of the way in which the same species is reconstructed by different writers or assembled by various museums, it will be immediately clear that many " solutions " are possible and that these do not necessarily include the correct one.

Reconstruction of the skeleton is a necessary prerequisite for reconstruction of the whole animal. It is clear that the latter also presents the palaeontologist with great and sometimes insoluble problems when it is remembered that important external characteristics such as the trunks of elephants, camels' humps, and types of coat and coloration are not reflected in the skeleton. If the mammoth had been known only from its skeleton, it would probably never have been reconstructed with a fatty hump or a well-developed covering of hair (Fig. 11). Without the zebra, classified as a living fossil by the " Union internationale pour la protection de la nature ", primitive horses with striped hides might never have appeared in palaeontological literature.

Similar considerations also apply to many invertebrates and to plants. The number of tentacles of most fossil cephalopods is not known, and, with regard to plants, anyone who has observed the difference in form between an apple-tree and a pear-tree will realise that even with the requisite knowledge of roots, trunk,

branches, foliage, blossom and fruit, completely accurate reconstruction remains impossible.

This means that to prepare a reconstruction of any fossil
organism, a thorough knowledge of its physiology is a primary
requisite, and even then the work is extraordinarily intricate. It
can never be claimed that the result is any more than a possibility.
The danger is that many such reconstructions are reproduced
repeatedly so that they eventually come to be accepted as indubit-
ably authentic.

6. *The palaeontological record*

The likelihood of an organism becoming a fossil is determined
primarily by its structure and the environment in which it lives or
in which it comes to rest after death. Consequently the chances of
fossilisation differ greatly from one group of animals or plants to
another. The chances of different types of sediment being preserved
over a long period of time also vary considerably. Continental
deposits, particularly if they lie high above sea-level, are liable
to relatively fast erosion, so that any organic remains they may
have contained also disappear. On the other hand, a vast amount
of fossiliferous sediment lies under the oceans where it is almost
inaccessible to the geologist. All this results in an uneven representation of the various plant and animal groups in the palaeontological record. A glance at Fig. 12 will immediately demonstrate
this. The insects are an obvious example of a group which, for
reasons of structure and environment, generally has poor chances
of fossilisation. Only a very small number of fossil species is
known, although more than 75 per cent of all recent species belong
to this group. Even if it is assumed that the insects are now at the
peak of their development, the number of fossil species of a group
that has existed since the Carboniferous must be many times

Fig. 11 (*opposite*). Various reconstructions of the mammoth (*Mammuthus
primigenius*). 1, skeleton, after Felix; 2, after a reconstruction by Figuier,
1863; 3, after a reconstruction by Pfizenmayer, 1905; 4, after a reconstruction
by Osborn, c. 1910: 5, after a reconstruction by Dietrich, 1912; 6, after a
reconstruction by Abel, 1912; 7, after a reconstruction by Knight, 1935;
8, after a picture by contemporaries: cave-painting, Font-de-Gaume, Dor-
dogne, from Bandi and Matinger. Note particularly the differences in coat
and shape: fatty hump, sloping back, and the height of the body above the
feet.

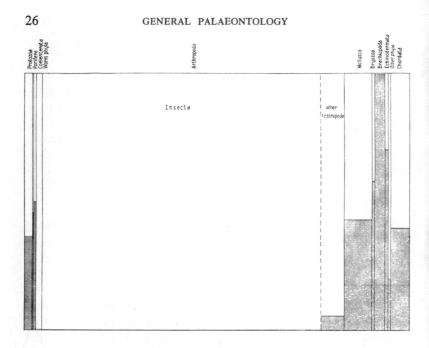

Fig. 12. Relation between the numbers of fossil species (shaded) and recent species (unshaded). The widths of the columns are proportional to the total number of species in the respective groups.

greater than is known at present. Many fossil insects are exclusive to a limited number of localities where exceptional circumstances of fossilisation have existed, and the number of specimens, as well as the number of species, is accordingly small.

Quite a different picture is provided by a group such as the brachiopods. These marine animals have favourable chances of fossilisation because of their hard shells and their habitat in the sub-littoral zone. Compared with 30,000 fossil species, approximately 200 recent species exist. The brachiopods as a group are long past the peak of their development; of the more than 1000 known fossil genera, the great majority dates from Palaeozoic times. The trend becomes even clearer if the higher systematic categories are considered. In the Silurian 19 superfamilies have been distinguished, 18 in the Devonian, but by the latter part of the Palaeozoic, in the Permian, the number is already down to 13. In the Trias there were still nine superfamilies, but today there are six. Only one new

superfamily has appeared since the Devonian, namely the Tere-
bratellacea in the Trias. It can safely be assumed, therefore,
that the number of species existing simultaneously at any time in
the Palaeozoic must have been many times greater than today.
This also shows that by no means all the brachiopod species that
once existed are known as fossils. If it is assumed that in the 600
million years' history of the brachiopods no more than 200 species
have existed simultaneously, and that a species survives on average
for one million years (a point that will be returned to in Chapter
5) a total of 120,000 species is reached. In other words the actual
number of fossil species must have been much greater than the
30,000 known at present, and if it is remembered that the brachiopods as a group were formerly much more important than they
are today, an even greater number of fossil species is possible. It
is hardly surprising then that the palaeontological record of many
groups with less favourable chances of fossilisation than the
brachiopods is no more than fragmentary. In the mammals, a
group whose chances of fossilisation vary—they possess hard parts
but are mainly confined to the land—the ratio between fossil and
recent species is approximately 1 : 1. Although the mammals
generally are probably past the peak of their evolution, the number
of fossil species known is still far smaller than might be expected
for a group that has formed such an important element in the
world's fauna for 60 to 70 million years.

The fact that new species of fossil organisms are discovered
daily confirms the incompleteness of present palaeontological
knowledge. Two other arguments point in the same direction.
Firstly, it is apparent that even recent flora and fauna are far from
being completely known. According to Mayr, Linsley and Usinger
(1953) new species of plants are being described at a rate of 5000
per year, and new animal species, including subspecies, at approximately 10,000 per year. Although few new species are likely to be
discovered in such groups as the mammals and the birds, there are
other groups of which only a relatively small part is known at
the moment. The number of known species of recent insects
amounts to a little less than one million, while the estimates of the
number at present inhabiting the Earth range up to three million
species.

Secondly, mention should be made of Schilder's calculations

(1942) based on data from population statistics. If a fauna consists of 60 species, then approximately 50,000 examples are necessary for there to be a reasonable chance of encountering its rarer components. Therefore in most cases it cannot be assumed on the basis of the palaeontological material available that the fauna of a particular locality is fully known. This is confirmed by new species being discovered at long-known and well-studied localities.

It would be incorrect, however, to deduce from these observations that palaeontology does not furnish a generally representative picture of life on Earth since the Cambrian. The fact that the greater part of all new discoveries corroborates existing knowledge supports this view. Only a small part of such discoveries implies a fundamental addition to present knowledge.

It is immediately clear from palaeontological evidence that there are gaps in present knowledge of some groups. The oldest known remains of birds come from the Upper Jurassic. These are the three famous specimens of *Archaeopteryx,* found in 1861, 1877 and 1959. Nothing more is known of Jurassic birds. The fossil birds of the Cretaceous are already so different from *Archaeopteryx* that it can only be assumed that an important part of the history of the birds remains unknown.

Similar hiatuses exist in the palaeontological record of other groups, sometimes spanning a very long period of time. For example, the Ciliata, a class of Protozoa, are known as fossils from the Jurassic and the Lower Cretaceous, and are not encountered again until the Pleistocene. Sometimes the history of an entire group is missing, the group being known only from recent species. Examples are various worm phyla, the subphylum Entoprocta of the Bryozoa, the subphylum Ctenophora of the Coelenterates, etc.

Gaps in the palaeontological record sometimes come to light through the discovery of recent representatives of groups long thought to be extinct. One example of this is the order of Crossopterygii—fish which flourished in the Devonian and, with the exception of one suborder, disappeared from the scene before the end of the Palaeozoic. This suborder, the Coelacanthina, is known from the Cretaceous with a few other, scarcely more advanced species. It was generally assumed that with these species the group had died out, until in 1938 a recent representative (*Latimeria*) was caught in the Indian Ocean. Even more interesting is the discovery made a few years ago by the Danish Galathea expedition off the coast of Mexico at a depth of 3600 metres. This was a recent representative (*Neopilina galatheae*) of the Tryblidiacea, a group of primitive patellaceous molluscs which are only known as fossils from Devonian and older rocks. The new, recent species resembles the Silurian genus *Pilina* so closely that only the great difference in age tipped the balance in favour of creating a new genus for it.

Both *Latimeria* and *Neopilina* are examples of what are generally termed living fossils—recent representatives of groups whose zenith lies far behind them. Such "survivors" generally represent an archaic type. Their continued existence is mostly the result of migration to an area of less competition. In the case of the two examples quoted, the ocean depths have presumably provided just such a protective environment. The same factor is apparently responsible for the absence of fossil representatives, since deep-sea fossil sediments are not very well known. The primitive mammals of the Australian continent form another example of living fossils.

New finds sometimes show that the history of a group continued longer than was at first supposed. The discovery of localities rich in fossils in the Permian of Timor at the beginning of this century suddenly shed new light on the palaeontology of various groups, as, for example, the crinoids, of which approximately 240 species were discovered in the Permian of Timor. This increased the total number of known fossil crinoids by 12 per cent. Of the 56 Timorian genera, 12 had hitherto been known only from the Carboniferous. Even more striking is the case of the blastoids which had previously been supposed to have become extinct at the end of the Lower Carboniferous. From the discoveries made on Timor it appears that this group experienced a distinct peak in Permian times: the 22 genera previously known were increased by 50 per cent.

Surprising discoveries like these will undoubtedly also be made in the future. If the number of new discoveries made in intensively studied areas such as Europe and North America is considered, it becomes obvious that those continents which so far have been only cursorily investigated have not yet disclosed all their secrets. The greater part of the new discoveries, however, should entail a gradual extension of existing knowledge rather than fundamental changes within the present framework. In other words, discoveries which bring to light entirely new higher categories, or place existing higher categories in periods where they had not previously been encountered, will probably remain exceedingly rare.

Although experience would suggest that the present view of past life on Earth is reasonably accurate in outline, this does not mean that the picture approximates *quantitively* to reality. A simple calculation based on the number of living species in existence at any given time (a), the average duration of a species (b) and the total duration of life on Earth (c), will make this point clear. The product of $a \times c$, divided by b will then give the total number of species. Simpson has made a similar calculation for the animal kingdom. He assumes that the total number of recent species, because of particular external circumstances (tectogenesis, high relief, climatic zones, fluctuations of climate and ice ages) is abnormally high. He therefore takes a maximum of 1,000,000 and a minimum of 250,000 contemporaneous living species. Putting the average duration of a species at between 5,000,000 and 500,000 years and the total duration of life on Earth between one and two thousand million years, he arrives at a total number of species between fifty millions (least favourable combination) and four thousand millions (most favourable combination). Cailleux produced a calculation in which he assumed a gradual increase such as would cause the number of species to be doubled every 80 million years. Putting the number of recent species at four million, which is at least double the number known, and the total duration of life on Earth at less than two thousand million years, he arrived at a total number of species of between 860 and 17 millions. These totals are, of course, smaller than Simpson's, but nevertheless they come within a comparable order of size.

Two obvious conclusions may be drawn from these figures: firstly, that the discovery of new species will continue for a long time yet, and secondly, that the picture of life on Earth will always remain quantitively incomplete. This is especially true, of course, of groups which, because of their structure and their environment, have unfavourable chances of fossilisation.

7. *Taxonomy and nomenclature*

As the remains of plants and animals, fossils are subject to the rules of nomenclature and classification which are applied in botany and zoology. Taxonomy or systematics is the branch of science particularly concerned with this. Taxonomy is at the same time the most elementary and the most advanced of all the organic sciences. It is elementary because it would be impossible to deal with so extensive a subject as fossil and recent plants and animals without giving names and creating order by means of a well-defined system of classification. It is advanced because classification should be based not on external characteristics but rather on relationship, that is to say it should be a reflection of phylogenetic history which comes not at the beginning but at the end of the study. Distinction is made between α, β and γ taxonomy, concerned respectively with the identification and naming of species, with their classification into higher categories, and with the study of intraspecific variation and evolution.

The rules of zoological nomenclature are based on the "International Code of zoological nomenclature" as adopted by the XV International Congress of Zoology (London 1958). The International Commission on Zoological Nomenclature acts as a permanent authority with regard to the application of the Code. It has its own official organ, the *Bulletin of Zoological Nomenclature*. A new edition of the French text and the English text of the Code was published in 1961. A survey even of the most important articles of the present Code is beyond the scope of this book.

Two questions of more general importance, however, deserve some attention: (*i*) the species concept in palaeontology and (*ii*) the connection between taxonomy and phylogeny.

The species is the basis of systematics and, in consequence, is its most important category, not only for the systematist, but for anyone who has to deal with the subject in one way or another. In principle there is no distinction between a recent and an extinct species. Unfortunately, however, there is all too often a difference in the way in which the concept "species" is used by the neontologist and the palaeontologist. The palaeontologist usually has only a part of an organism at his disposal—and sometimes not a particularly essential part. It is a dead object, often bearing little relation to the environment in which it lived. Consequently the species is primarily a morphological concept for the palaeontologist.

The neontologist on the other hand has a complete organism, usually a good number of them in fact, and he is moreover able to take geographical, ecological, physiological and genetic criteria into consideration when defining species. The last of these is very important since, in the words of Mayr, Linsley and Usinger (1953, p. 25), " Species are groups of actually (or potentially) interbreeding natural populations which are reproductively isolated from other such groups."

This " biological " species concept can hardly be employed in palaeontology. In neontology it reflects, after all, a point of view which is not particularly old and is often referred to as " the new systematics ", a term which dates from 1940 but indicates a concept already present among research workers in the second half of the last century. The species concept was formerly predominantly morphological in neontology too, where great value was placed on the type-specimen. In " the new systematics " much more extensive material is preferred, working with a sample, as it were, of the whole population which thus becomes the basic taxonomic unit. Today the interest of the systematist is therefore focused primarily on the subdivision of the species.

Can a similar modification of the species concept, from a morpho-typological to a " biological " point of view, be expected in palaeontology? Naturally such a change would be desirable, because the basic taxonomic unit is better delimited by the biological species concept than the morphological one. In neontology there are numerous examples of groups of individuals which are so similar that they could be classed as a single species, were it not known that they did not in fact fulfil the criterion of the biological definition of species. Conversely, many true species show such divergent characteristics that no palaeontologist would hesitate to classify them as two or more species.

The only question is whether such a modification of the species concept is possible. The answer depends on the material. If this is scarce, as is often the case with large vertebrates, the retention of the old morphological concept, the morphospecies, is unavoidable. It must be remembered, however, that the palaeontologist, especially in the case of the invertebrates, may have extensive material at his disposal. Probably the most has not been made of past opportunities, particularly as many specialist systematic palaeontologists did not collect their own material, but were limited to what they obtained from others who generally took the view that one specimen of a fossil was as good as 10 or 100. It is clear from much recent research (for example, that of Trueman and others on non-marine lamellibranchs of the Carboniferous) that examination of carefully collected and comprehensive material deepens understanding and helps to achieve in palaeontology the application of a species concept which tends towards the biospecies, even though not identical with it. The more representative the sample is of the population or populations provided by the material, the nearer the palaeontological species concept will approximate to the biospecies. As well as using statistical methods, which are an indispensable aid, the palaeontologist must analyse the manner in which fossils occur. Are they autochthonous, allochthonous or a mixture of both? Has transport, where it has taken place, acted selectively? These are no longer questions of systematics but of general palaeontology. The intimate connection now apparent between these two aspects of the subject forms, perhaps, the only justification for including a discussion on the species concept in a work on general palaeontology.

This might imply, as the foregoing argument seems to do, that the species concept of the palaeontologist will always be out of date compared with that of the neontologist. To believe this would be to lose sight of the fact that the palaeontologist is able to take account of an essential factor which the neontologist can only rarely introduce into his work, namely time. It is now realised that the species is not constant as Linnaeus thought, but it can hardly be said that the species concept of the neontologist has been greatly influenced by this most fundamental change. With the same ease which the neontologist can observe variation in a geographical sense, the palaeontologist can observe variation in a chronological sense, and if the latter is taken into account, a new concept, that of the chronospecies, emerges. If a sufficiently long interval of time is observed, gradual variation in a constant direction can produce a series whose initial and final members can no longer be classified in the same species, although at no point within the series can a definite dividing line be drawn. This will be referred to again in Chapter 5.

It is self-evident that carefully collected and comprehensive material is necessary for this sort of application of the species concept in palaeontology. This requirement cannot always be met, and consequently there is no question of a single species concept in palaeontology. The concepts of morphospecies, chronospecies and something resembling the biospecies are all employed. The natural predisposition and potentialities of the first workers to do research into a particular group often determine its subsequent theoretical basis, and a change in species concept generally necessitates a somewhat modified diagnosis which is difficult to introduce without coming into conflict with the existing code.

It is clear from the idea underlying the chronospecies that there are no hard and fast boundaries between species. Therefore the definition of species becomes largely a question of taste and experience. In palaeontology this applies equally to the horizontal delimitation of species, since the essential criterion of the biospecies is unusable. Consequently there are widely divergent ideas as to what constitutes a species in palaeontology. The extreme points of view are represented by the " splitters " and the " lumpers ". The former try to subdivide their material into as many species as possible, and the latter to limit the number of species as far as they are able. The lumpers are thus inclined to regard the differences observed between individuals as intraspecific variations, whilst the methods of the splitters have often meant that in practice the species has become a totally unusable unit, which can never be the aim of systematist. Even apart from such extreme instances, it must be admitted that there is a general tendency in palaeontology to create too many species. Numerous fossil species are exclusively based on a difference of stratigraphic or geological location, and the making of reliable correlations is thereby rendered unnecessarily difficult or even impossible.

It is not surprising, therefore, that an ever-increasing number of voices are heard which would put the emphasis on the practical usefulness of the species. Arkell and Moy-Thomas (in Huxley, ed., 1940) have given the following definition for palaeontology of the species as " a practical and convenient unit by which fossils are distinguished ".

Animals and plants can be classified according to some sort of system in many ways and by the application of many different criteria. The present, generally accepted position, that phylogeny alone forms the basis of a natural system, by no means implies that the difficulties inherent in the classification of organisms into a hierarchic system of categories are solved thereby. On the contrary, phylogeny is itself a branch of science which progresses slowly by the use of results obtained from many other sciences. Therefore a taxonomic system cannot be expected to be a reflection of phylogeny. What can be expected is that its differentiated units should be phylogenetic units whose distances apart in the system should be a measure of their phylogenetic relationship. Even if the phylogeny of a large group, the molluscs for example, were known to the last detail, it would appear possible to base several natural systems upon it. This must be even more the case if the phylogenetic relationships of a group are still largely unknown. Phylogeny, as such, cannot be observed based as it is upon the interpretation of facts which are usually amenable to various interpretations. A too literal reflection of phylogeny in classification would accordingly lead to continual revision. The system, as a means of achieving the convenient arrangement of a vast subject, would thereby be deprived of its usefulness. Or, in the words of Simpson, " Good classification is conservative " (1945, p. 13). This does not necessarily mean that modifications should remain in abeyance once a particular classification is in use. Changes should always be limited to those cases which rest on generally accepted changes of opinion. The value of a system depends largely on its practical usefulness and the degree to which it is accepted. Perhaps it would be as well to remember at this point that the species classified are subjective units to begin with, since they are derived from morphological units which are, perhaps, at best a distant reflection of a natural genetic unit.

CHAPTER 2

THE HORIZONTAL DISTRIBUTION OF FOSSILS: ECOLOGICAL FACTORS

1. *Ecology and palaeoecology*

Every organism has a definite relationship to its environment. The term " environment " is comprehensive and should be understood to embrace not only such physical and chemical factors as light, temperature, salinity and oxygen content, but also the other organisms, whether of the same or differing species, which exist there. Ecology is the branch of biology especially concerned with the relationship of animals and plants to their environment. In the same way, palaeoecology is the study of the relationship of fossil organisms to the environment in which they lived. There is, however, a difference between the ecological and palaeoecological method. The ecologist is able to acquaint himself in detail both with a flora and fauna, and with the physical and chemical conditions under which they live. By investigation in the field and experiment in the laboratory, he can then proceed to study the relationship between organisms and their environment, and the inter-relationship of the organisms themselves.

The palaeoecologist cannot work in this way. His knowledge of the flora and fauna is often far from complete, and he cannot acquaint himself with the conditions of the inorganic environment by direct observation and measurement; knowledge of these conditions is one of the ultimate aims of the palaeoecologist. In order to make inferences about the conditions which prevailed in a fossil environment he is obliged to start out from an incomplete picture of the total organic world and make use of assumptions borrowed from ecology. The difference in method between ecology and palaeoecology could be formulated as:

ecology: organisms + environment → relationship
palaeoecology: incomplete picture of organisms + hypothetical
relationship > environment

The palaeoecologist obviously has to build on none too firm a foundation. The fossils which make up his basic material represent a fortuitous selection of the total organic world; his data, based on the results of ecological investigation into the relationship of organism to environment, can be no more than hypothetical. The properties of the sediment itself naturally provide clues to the reconstruction of an environment. No-one would diagnose an anaerobic environment for a fauna encountered in well-graded sand with ripple marks. It is self-evident that every palaeoecological analysis of the organic component of a sediment—the fauna— should be accompanied by a close examination of the inorganic component: composition, distribution of grain-sizes and sedimentary features should be analysed. The reverse is equally true. Equal weight has not been given so far to these two complementary methods of arriving at the reconstruction of an environment: the "inorganic" method has been followed more often than the "organic", although the two are in fact interdependent.

Finally it is clear that acquaintance with and understanding of ecological data are indispensable for the palaeoecologist.

2. *Biocoenosis and thanatocoenosis*

Biocoenosis is the term used to indicate all the organisms inhabiting a particular environment. Only a part of the biocoenosis is preserved in a fossil state in the sediment and alien elements can be added to it by being transported there after death. The term thanatocoenosis is used to indicate all the fossils at a particular place in a sediment. Generally there is no direct connection between a thanatocoenosis and a biocoenosis.

A thanatocoenosis will usually consist of two groups of components: (*i*) the autochthonous component, being that part of the biocoenosis which is fossilised *in situ* in the sediment, and (*ii*) the allochthonous component, comprised of elements which did not normally inhabit the environment and arrived there, after active or passive transport, to be fossilised with the autochthonous component (*i*); in the case of passive transport such elements could already be in a fragmentary condition.

Fig. 13 gives an analysis in diagram form of the relationship between biocoenosis and thanatocoenosis. The component elements of a biocoenosis can in principle be divided into four parts, as far as their subsequent fate is concerned. One part (*a*) disappears

without trace at the place of death, another part (*b*) is fossilised
in situ. The rest is carried away, part of it (*c*) disappearing without
trace and part (*d*) being fossilised elsewhere. Naturally this last
part does not necessarily remain as an entity; it may be split up
during transport and be distributed amongst various thanatocoenoses. Furthermore, the element (*d*) may be entirely lacking in
a thanatocoenosis (autochthonous thanatocoenosis), while conversely the element (*b*) may be missing (allochthonous thanatocoenosis).

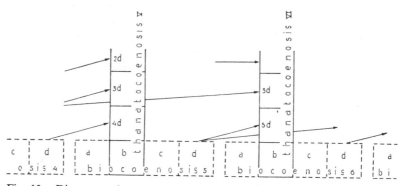

Fig. 13.   Diagrammatic representation of the relations between biocoenosis
and thanatocoenosis.

The alien elements mixed while still alive with the elements of
the first group form a remarkable borderline case between autochthony and allochthony. They have lived in the environment, physiologically speaking, although it is not in fact their normal habitat.
From the ecological point of view they have to be included with the
allochthonous group. The alien environment may even be the cause
of death, as is the case with certain elements of the Upper Jurassic
fauna of the Solnhofen Limestone. This is also true, perhaps, of
the large whales from the Miocene of Antwerp. It is known that
large recent whales, whose true habitat is in the oceans, are almost
invariably doomed if they stray into the North Sea.

From the palaeoecological viewpoint it is therefore desirable
that every thanatocoenosis should first be split into its autochthonous and allochthonous components.

3. *The analysis of thanatocoenosis*

In order to be able to separate a thanatocoenosis into its autochthonous and allochthonous components, two groups of questions must first be answered: (*i*) which fossils occur in the thanatocoenosis, and (*ii*) in what manner do they occur? The second question will be discussed first, as part of the answer has to be found in the field.

Fossils may be found singly or in great accumulations; species by species or intermixed; graded according to size or with various sizes appearing haphazardly together; orientated in a particular manner or distributed at random. Relevant data can contribute considerably to a correct understanding of the origins of a thanatocoenosis, and, therefore, to a knowledge of the environment and the conditions in which sedimentation occurred. This being so, it is remarkable that these questions are so often ignored in palaeontological research. Many monographs on celebrated localities have nothing to say concerning the manner in which fossils occur in the sediment.

In some deposits only isolated fossils are encountered, yet their distribution throughout the sediment may be regular. In others accumulations of fossils occur, sometimes to the extent of forming the greater part of the sediment, as, for example, in places in the Plio-Pleistocene Crag deposits of East Anglia, and the so-called bryozoan bed in the Maastrichtian of South Limburg in the Netherlands. Accumulations of this kind sometimes consist of a single species, sometimes of a number.

In many deposits fossils are found concentrated in certain beds which are interspersed with others where they are either much less plentiful or entirely absent. The thickness and composition of such highly fossiliferous beds can vary considerably, ranging from strata of a few decimetres, or even a metre or more in thickness, to others that are no more than the thickness of one fossil—the fossils lie side by side arranged in one plane. The fossil content of such strata often consists entirely of examples of one species (Plate 1) and sometimes even of individuals of approximately equal dimensions (Plate 2). Strata of this sort, occurring at different levels in the same section, sometimes look alike, but in detail they are usually seen to contain either different

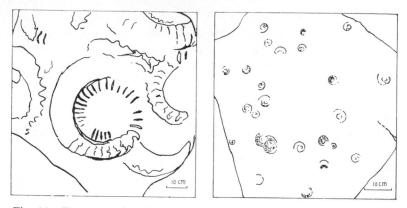

Fig. 14. Two examples of concentrations of ammonites of approximately equal size, in the Lias of Dorset.

species or individuals of different dimensions (Fig. 14). Recent examples of such layers can be seen on many beaches along the North Sea coast.

There is great variation not only in the manner in which fossils are distributed, but also in their orientation with regard to the structural and textural features of the sediment.

Most fossils with a clearly developed longitudinal axis, such as many gastropods and belemnites, or with more than one longitudinal axis, as, for example, the valves or shells of lamellibranchs,

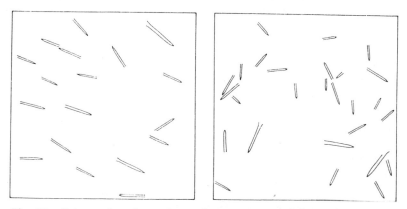

Fig. 15. Orientated and unorientated arrangement of belemnites, in the Lias of Dorset and Yorkshire respectively.

PLATE 1

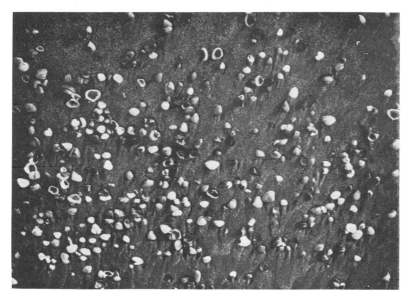

Concentration of loose lamellibranch valves. Recent, North Sea beach. Most of the valves lie convex side uppermost.

Concentration of brachiopod valves of one species and approximately equal dimensions. Carboniferous, Northumberland.

PLATE 2

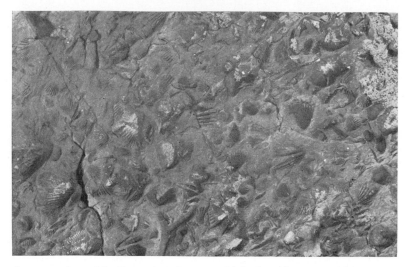

Concentration of badly graded elements, chiefly brachiopods and bryozoans. 5/8 actual size. Lebanza Limestone, Lower Devonian, Cantabrian Mountains.

Concentration of small elements, chiefly algae, brachiopods, and bryozoans. 1/2 actual size. Same locality as above, but about 1 foot higher in the section.

ammonites and brachiopods, lie with their longitudinal axes parallel to the stratification. In bivalve shells, such as those of lamellibranchs and brachiopods, it is important to note whether both valves are present, how they lie in relation to each other—closed, open, or completely extended—and also how the valves are orientated in relation to the upper and lower surfaces of the strata, whether the concave or the convex side is uppermost. Fossils with one longitudinal axis are sometimes arranged roughly parallel to each other, thus displaying a particular orientation on bedding planes in plan view. In other cases, the long axis, or axes, may be orientated more or less perpendicularly to the bedding planes of the sediment.

All data of this sort are important when attempting to determine which part of a thanatocoenosis is autochthonous and which allochthonous.

Autochthony can be most clearly demonstrated in plant fossils when fragments of trunks or stems remain in their original positions with their roots. The Carboniferous *Stigmaria* beds and the root-zones of *Lepidodendron* species form a well-known example, but similar natural positions are known from many other deposits, such as Miocene lignite and Holocene peat.

Amongst invertebrates the clearest indications of autochthony occur with animals that burrow in the sea-bed, particularly lamellibranchs. There have apparently been very few burrowing brachiopods. Craig has described *Lingula* sitting in vertical burrows with their pedicles still present, from the Carboniferous of Scotland.

The shells of burrowing lamellibranchs generally attain certain morphological characteristics, including a strongly marked sinus in the pallial line caused by the presence of a long siphon, gaping valves and often in addition an elongated shell form. The recent *Solen* is an extreme example of this. If such shells are found in

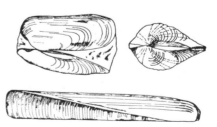

FIG. 16
A few burrowing lamellibranchs: *Palaeosolen* from the Devonian (above); *Pholadomya* from the Upper Cretaceous (left); and *Endodesma* from the Silurian (right). After Dacqué.

a vertical position in the sediment with their siphon apertures upwards, it may be safely concluded that they are autochthonous.

Burrowing animals from various groups, such as arthropods, echinoderms and worms are found among the recent benthonic fauna of all types of areas of sand and mud deposition. There is no reason to assume that this was otherwise in former times. Nevertheless few of these creatures are known as fossils, although they might be expected to have very good chances of fossilisation. Many examples of fossilised burrows are known, but these seldom contain the remains of the creatures that made them. It is not usually possible to ascribe such burrows to a particular species, as both U-shaped and straight passages are made by animals of a wide systematic range. The absence of remains may partly be because the animal lacked hard parts, as in the case of worms, but this explanation does not apply to all invertebrates. Sometimes, of course, the creature itself is preserved in a recognisable state, but not the burrow which may have caved in after the occupant's death, become filled up or flattened in. Perhaps a more careful investigation of suitable sediments will bring to light more examples of such burrowing species. Apart from lamellibranchs, the number of examples so far described is very small.

Non-burrowing benthonic forms can sometimes be identified as autochthonous elements of a thanatocoenosis, especially sessile species; apart from plants this mode of life is practically confined to aquatic invertebrates, amongst which there are many sessile groups. Concentrations of these benthonic animals often occur. The recent beds of mussels and cockles on tidal flat areas are a good example of this.

In some cases attachment to the substratum is effected by means of the soft parts of the animal, such as the pedicles of brachiopods or the byssal threads of many Anisomyaria (lamellibranchs), in other cases by direct contact of the shell or skeleton, as for example in corals, crinoids and in such lamellibranchs as oysters and rudists. In the latter case the chances of fossilisation *in situ* are naturally much greater, as the hard parts remain in position after the animal's death. When attachment is by means of soft parts, the hard parts will probably be dislodged and transported after death, making the establishment of autochthony difficult. Nevertheless fossil examples are known of animals which attach themselves to

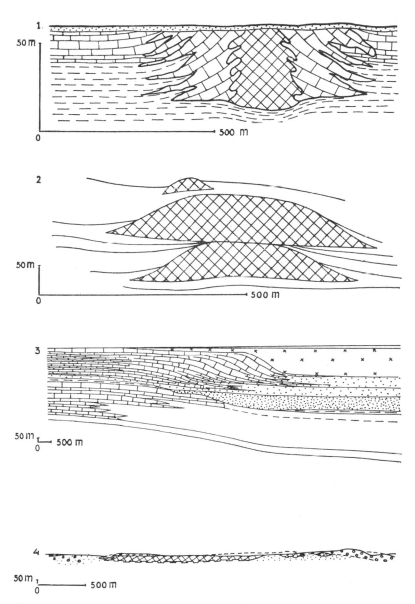

Fig. 17. Examples (in section) of various types of reefs, chiefly built by corals. From top to bottom: 1. reef of an unstable area with well-developed detrital deposits along its flanks (Silurian, Indiana, after Cummings and Shrock); 2. succession of small reefs (Upper Devonian, Ardennes, after Lecompte); 3. transverse section through a barrier reef (Capitan Reef, Permian, Texas, after King); 4. flat reef (biostrome) in a stable area (Upper Jurassic, Paris basin, after Rutten and Jansonius).

43

the substratum by their soft parts. The beds of brachiopods in some Mesozoic deposits are an example. In such cases it must be assumed either that the animals were buried while still alive by sediment which subsequently killed them or that they were covered so soon after death as to be fixed in their original position. In lamellibranchs the matter can sometimes be settled by looking at the relative positions of the valves, since these are opened by tension in the ligament as soon as the adductor muscle no longer functions. If, therefore, sediment appears to have been deposited in the normal manner between the opened valves, it is unlikely that death resulted from covering by sediment.

Animals living in colonies are sometimes packed so close together that growth is hindered. Abnormalities in the shell form of two adjacent specimens can often demonstrate autochthony.

Of animals which are attached directly to the substratum by their hard parts, the reef-builders should be mentioned first: corals, stromatoporoids, sponges and calcareous algae. Large structures of these groups, separately or in combination, may always be regarded as autochthonous but caution is necessary with small structures. When deciding whether the latter are autochthonous or allochthonous, their shape and their position relative to the sediment must be considered. The form of these organic structures, usually indicated by the general term reef, can vary considerably. In addition to the familiar inverted dish-shaped reefs, as in the Frasnian of the southern synclinorium of Dinant, much flatter, or less regularly shaped ones occur (Figs. 17, 18, 19).

In addition to reef-building organisms, there are many other animals whose hard parts are directly attached to the substratum, as, for example, certain lamellibranchs—including rudists—crinoids and a number of the brachiopods. All these may, dependent on local circumstances, indicate the autochthony of the elements concerned.

Finally fossil tracks must of course be regarded as autochthonous because they cannot be displaced. The difficulty is that it cannot usually be established what type of animal made them. In this respect the study of recent tracks is of great importance to palaeontology. Occasionally tracks are found with the fossilised animal at the end of them, which not only dispels doubt about the originator of the trail, but also establishes the animal's autochthony. Autochthony in the strict sense of the word does not always include autochthony in the ecological sense. The possibility of ecologically alien elements must always be borne in mind. This applies to a number of fossils lying at the end of their tracks in the Solnhofen limestone deposits. Walther and Abel have shown that these died because they entered an unsuitable environment.

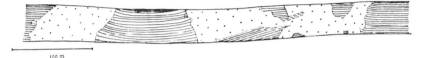

Fig. 18. Section through sponge reefs in the Upper Jurassic of South Germany. After Roll.

Fig. 19. Section through a bryozoan, or an algal-bryozoan, reef in the Permian of Durham. After Trechman.

It can be seen therefore that autochthonous fossils occur exclusively among benthonic forms. All other animals undergo vertical displacement at least before reaching the sedimentation area with its favourable chances of fossilisation. Among benthonic animals, those with a sessile mode of life have the greatest likelihood, and most easily demonstrable chance of *in situ* fossilisation.

With allochthonous fossils there is always some degree of transport, although this may be limited to dropping vertically to the ground or the sea-bed. As with clastic particles, transport generally leads to selection as well as to a particular orientation of the transported material. It is these two transport phenomena that usually provide proof of allochthony, moreover mechanical damage may be an indication of transport. Concerning fossil orientation, a primary distinction should be made between sedimentation from a fluid and from a static medium.

When after transport organic remains of elongated form are deposited from a fluid medium, they come to rest with their longitudinal axes parallel to the direction of the current, as with gastropod shells, belemnites, etc. The arms of starfish or crinoids may also display parallel orientation. Dish-shaped bodies, such as the detached valves of brachiopods and lamellibranchs, generally settle with their convex side uppermost. This is an important criterion for the recognition of transport, and, consequently, of allochthony. Many fossil beds consisting of accumulations of brachiopod or lamellibranch valves present this aspect. The seashore provides a recent example: the greater part of the lamellibranch valves left by the tide lie convex side uppermost. Exceptions to this rule can sometimes be caused by an abnormal position of the centre of gravity: the pedicle valves of pentamerid brachiopods with well developed spondylium generally lie convex side downwards.

The current direction of a medium can usually be deduced from the orientation of its fossils. This presents no difficulty with the arms of starfish or crinoids. Cone-shaped gastropod shells may lie with either their bases or their apices pointing in the direction of the current, depending on whether they came to rest freely, or through obstruction. Matters are less obvious in the case of dish-shaped bodies. Trusheim's experiments showed that some lamellibranch species are deposited with the umbo pointing in the direction of the current, others in the reverse position, without it being clear what factors had determined orientation. Finally it should be pointed out that lack of any prevailing orientation pattern does not necessarily argue against a fluid medium. Turbulence, for example, may produce a random orientation.

A random orientation is also generally displayed by elongated organic remains coming to rest in a stationary medium under the pull of gravity. Dish-shaped bodies, however, will settle with their convex sides uppermost in these circumstances.

It is apparent therefore that an analysis of the distribution and orientation of fossils in a sediment provides valuable data for the correct understanding of a thanatocoenosis. The identification of one part of its component elements as autochthonous, and of the other as allochthonous sometimes leads directly to a delimitation of the environment in which the thanatocoenosis was formed. Obviously a thanatocoenosis can consist entirely of autochthonous or entirely of allochthonous elements. If both are present, immediate allocation of all the elements to one or other of the two groups is not always possible and an unclassified remainder will usually be left for further study.

The second question is which fossils occur in the thanatocoenosis. This can only be answered by a thorough and systematic examination of the material available. Depending on the extent and state of preservation of the latter, this should enable identification to be carried out—preferably as far as the species level.

An ecological interpretation of the fauna or flora is the next step. This is a hazardous undertaking, since conclusions are partly based on analogies with recent representatives of the groups in question. The recent reef-building corals of the Zoantharia cannot tolerate water temperatures below 18°C. They are consequently restricted to the zone lying between 25° North and 25° South, and within this zone they require certain conditions of depth and clarity of water. It is generally assumed that fossil reef-building Zoantharia which are known from the Trias onward required similar environmental conditions. This assumption is justified by the close relationship of all the Mesozoic and Cainozoic reef-building coral species, but it carries less conviction if extended to the Palaeozoic reef-building corals, such as the Tabulata, whose relationship to the Zoantharia is not entirely clear; it is possible, but it does not necessarily follow, that the Palaeozoic corals required the same conditions.

Fortunately there are two sets of factors which provide a firmer basis for the reconstruction of an environment. Firstly, the properties of the sediment itself and the geological pattern of the region furnish a starting point. Inferences made from the organic and inorganic components of a sediment can therefore be checked against each other. These should be mutually compatible for a reliable reconstruction of the environment. Secondly, many groups differ from the corals in that there is a definite connection between the environment and the characteristics of the hard parts with which the palaeontologist generally has to work. This important point will be returned to in Section 6.

A thanatocoenosis will generally be found to contain various fossil groups which could not have lived in the same environment. This provides a new criterion for splitting a thanatocoenosis into its autochthonous and allochthonous components, even if it is not immediately apparent which of the mutually exclusive groups represents the indigenous and which the exotic element. It is generally possible to solve this problem, however, by examining the data concerning the distribution and position of the fossils in the sediment and the characteristics of the sediment itself. A further criterion is provided by the biological age, reflected in their size, reached by the fossil individuals of each species. It has been shown already that the natural arrangement of numbers of examples according to size is an indication of transport. Conversely, the occurrence in a thanatocoenosis of individuals of different sizes, that is to say of varying biological age, is often a useful argument for autochthony.

To recapitulate, it is evident that the analysis of a thanatocoenosis into its autochthonous and allochthonous parts is a necessary precondition of a correct reconstruction of its environment. It is the autochthonous components, always compatible with the sediment, that determine the environment. This does not mean that the allochthonous elements give no indication of environment; the negative evidence they provide can sometimes be valuable. Much more important, however, is the fact that these exotic elements were able to reach their ultimate place of fossilisation. It is therefore important to define their environment more closely. The greater the allochthonous part of the thanatocoenosis, the easier the connection and the closer the original environment of the exotic element must have been; the proximity of a coastline can generally be inferred from the presence of an obviously terrestrial component in a palpably marine thanatocoenosis.

4. *Environments*

The primary concern of the ecologist is to analyse the relationship of recent organisms to their environment. This relationship which is only partially understood at present and the incomplete fossil record of former floras and faunas form the basis of the palaeoecologist's research into the nature of the fossil environment. For the ecologist, an environment is determined by both inorganic and organic factors—by physical and chemical factors, as well as by the living organisms that inhabit it. The nature of the medium (air or water) and of the substratum, the temperature, light, oxygen and carbon dioxide content are the most important of the inorganic factors. Rivers, lakes and seas have a common medium even though there are important differences in their respective chemical compositions. The first and most obvious distinction to make however is that between continental and marine environments because the coastline assumes such a dominant position in any geological study of an environment. Continental environments can have either air or water as a medium. Continental sediments account for relatively few sedimentary rocks and sub-aerial deposits are an unfavourable medium for fossilisation. From the palaeontological point of view, aquatic areas within a large continental environment, such as rivers, lakes or marshes are of greater significance,

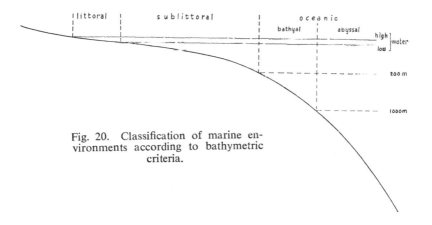

Fig. 20. Classification of marine environments according to bathymetric criteria.

not only for aquatic flora and fauna, but also for that of the adjacent land areas. Knowledge of typical land flora and fauna is based largely on remains found in aquatic sediments. The sedimentation and the regional geological pattern are important criteria in the identification of these deposits.

The essential factor that must be taken into account in the definition of continental environments is the nature of the medium. If this is water, the first question is whether it is stagnant or running. Otherwise, the same factors are operative as in marine environments: light, temperature, oxygen content, etc.

A subdivision of marine environments can be made according to various criteria. Using depth as the first, four zones can be distinguished: a littoral zone between the high and low tide marks; a sublittoral zone from the low tide mark to approximately 200 metres;[1] a bathyal zone to approximately 100 metres; and an abyssal zone with a depth of more than 1000 metres. The deepest oceanic trenches below 4500 or 5000 metres are often referred to as nadal. The 200-metre limit corresponds roughly to the outer edge of the continental shelf, the geophysical boundary of the continents. From the ecological or physiological angle, this boundary is important as it is approximately the depth to which light penetrates. In the sublittoral zone, therefore, the sea-bed still receives a certain amount of light.

This subdivision which is capable of further refinement is purely bathymetric. If attention is turned to the mode of life of marine organisms, a primary distinction can be made between those that live on or in the sea-bed (benthonic organisms, the benthos) and those that live and move freely in the water (pelagic organisms).[2] It is therefore possible to speak of the littoral benthos, the sublittoral benthos and so on. A subdivision of this sort has less point for the pelagic organisms, although terms like epipelagic and bathypelagic for organisms living in the upper 200 metres of the sea and between 200 and 1000 metres respectively are sometimes useful. The greater number of pelagic organisms inhabit the upper 600 metres of the sea. Below this depth, the density of population decreases greatly, although living creatures do occur. There is point in dividing pelagic organisms into those that move actively (the nekton) and those that float or drift passively (the plankton).

The most important physical and chemical factors governing life in the sea are the movement of the water, the temperature, the amount of solid substances, the salinity and the oxygen content, and, possibly, of other gases in solution. For benthonic species, there are two additional factors of importance: depth and the constitution of the sea-bed. These factors are so vital that the environmental control of benthonic organisms is much greater than that of pelagic species whose environmental limits are far less critical. The various factors which together determine the

---

[1] The littoral and the sublittoral zone together are usually referred to as the neritic zone, although this term originally had a different significance. Haeckel, who introduced the term, used it to indicate not a depth zone, but the mode of life of those creatures that for part of their lives are pelagic and part sessile benthonic.

[2] It follows from this that the much-used expression " pelagic sediments " is a particularly unfortunate combination of two concepts and should be avoided.

physical and chemical circumstances of an environment are inter-related. Oxygen content, for example, is directly connected with the movement of the water which in turn is partly responsible for the character of the sediment.

The movement of water is particularly important as an ecological factor in the littoral zone and in the highest part of the sublittoral zone where mechanical factors limit the distribution of fragile organisms.

Light is an important factor in all zones because photosynthesis in plants is dependent upon it, which in turn form the basis of all animal life. Temperature is not only of climatological importance: it also determines the solubility of calcium carbonate.

The amount of solid substances is generally significant only in the layers of water nearest the sea-bed, but it can be considerable in higher water layers, for example near the mouth of estuaries. Some animal groups, such as corals, display great sensitivity to this factor.

Although the salinity of sea-water is generally constant, special circumstances may cause it to rise or fall. If evaporation exceeds the access of sea-water, salinity rises. Increasing salinity alone will cause an impoverishment of the fauna. Such salinity changes, however, normally occur in landlocked basins which are in any case geographically isolated and it may be difficult to separate the influence of the two factors. This can be seen in Western Europe in the impoverished fauna of the Zechstein. An excessive inflow of fresh water causes a drop in salinity. As a rule this also causes an impoverishment of the fauna and leads to the development of thin-shelled forms and dwarfed varieties.

Oxygen content is ecologically one of the most important environmental factors. Palaeontologically, however, this factor is difficult to assess, as long as it does not drop below a certain critical value when it causes very specialised environmental conditions, of which euxinic basins are an extreme example.

The substratum is a factor of great significance for benthonic organisms because of its effect on their mode of life (burrowing, boring, attachment) and their food supply. It is well known that many benthonic animals derive their food from the sediment, particularly from the fine-grained parts. In the shallower environments of the littoral and sublittoral zones the supply of sediment is bound up with the movement of water.

The littoral zone represents a specialised environment because all the sessile benthonic organisms must be able to survive a certain time out of the water, which varies according to their position in the zone. The littoral zone, in spite of its shallowness, therefore displays a finely-graded series of subzones. It is here, moreover, that the mechanical forces of water movement often reach their maximum.

5. *Different types of thanatocoenosis*

As a community of living organisms in a particular environment, a biocoenosis undergoes a continual process of rejuvenation. Its character may be changed in the course of time, either by external or internal factors (succession), but the biocoenosis itself does not die. A thanatocoenosis, however, is generally the product of mechanical forces. It is not subject to evolution, but fixes and records a particular moment in a partly organic, partly inorganic development.

Consequently there is a clear distinction between the biocoenosis and the thanatocoenosis with regard to time, and also with regard to space. Whilst the vertical extent of a biosphere in the atmosphere and hydrosphere is considerable, all thanatocoenoses are restricted to the ground, or to the sea or river beds. A tree-top biocoenosis, for example, is never transferred *in situ* to a thanatocoenosis and the same applies to every pelagic biocoenosis. The allochthonous components of a thanatocoenosis have moreover been subjected to the laws of transport and sedimentation, and this imposes a further limitation on many thanatocoenoses with regard to space—an important point, as wholly or predominantly allochthonous thanatocoenoses are quantitatively very significant.

Like environments, thanatocoenoses can be divided into continental and marine. Land thanatocoenoses are rare because of a combination of various factors including scanty sedimentation and dissolution of organic remains. It is not surprising that the finest-grained land sediments furnish the best thanatocoenoses; among these are the gastropod and mammal remains in loess deposits. Aeolian sands, such as dunes, rarely contain fossils.

In addition to these there are purely land thanatocoenoses of a rather unusual character, such as in cave and fissure deposits. These are limited spatially, but their relative wealth of organic remains makes them important; the significance of cave deposits in Pleistocene geology is well known and the often massive accumulations of animal remains in fissure deposits are similarly important.

Of greater significance than purely land thanatocoenoses are those of land surface waters. The remains of land animals and plants, as well as of aquatic organisms, are usually to be found in fluvial and lacustrine thanatocoenoses. Land organisms may predominate in these thanatocoenoses; there are many examples of aquatic thanatocoenoses consisting entirely of allochthonous land elements, and knowledge of fossil land floras and faunas is largely based on these.

Fluvial and lacustrine thanatocoenoses are distinguished from each other by their different water movement patterns. Fluvial deposits are in general recognisable from their sedimentation pattern, but the distinction is often most difficult to make in the fossiliferous parts of the sediment. The stream-bed of a river obviously offers less favourable conditions for fossilisation than areas of quieter sedimentation, but it is in these areas that the sedimentary pattern most resembles that of lacustrine deposits. The two types of environment are also connected by transitional areas. Dead channels are regarded as lakes, except in times of flood, when they may again form part of the river system. On the other hand lakes are often a permanent part of river systems, especially in the upper courses, as is the case with many of the Swiss lakes.

The most favourable areas for fossils to be found are in ox-bow lakes and other similar formations, on flooded banks and in the lower reaches of rivers where the velocity of the current is greatly reduced, particularly the higher parts of deltas with their many shifting channels. Estuarine deposits and the lower regions of deltas often display a marked, and sometimes predominant marine influence; thanatocoenoses here are generally mixed in character, the continental element decreasing seawards. Interesting palaeogeographical conclusions can be drawn from an estimate of the respective proportions of continental and marine elements in a series of thanatocoenoses of equal age.

Fluvial thanatocoenoses are well known. In the Netherlands the fossil deposits in the Lower Pleistocene clay of Tegelen and the Middle Pleistocene clay of Nede, with their characteristic mixture of aquatic and land fossils, must be regarded as originating in the quieter parts of river systems. Similar thanatocoenoses are also found higher up the Rhine basin.

Recent examples of thanatocoenoses characteristic of fluvial floods are plentiful, but fossil examples are rare presumably owing to the combination of conflicting factors necessary for their consolidation. These alluvial thanatocoenoses which are also a feature of lacustrine and marine conditions consist of material washed together and deposited, generally on the bank, where the medium can no longer transport it. The higher the water-level, the higher the zone of washed-up material will extend. The chances of this type of thanatocoenosis becoming fossilised depend on how quickly the material is covered by sediment. The higher parts of the bank are only rarely reached by the water and the thanatocoenosis disappears before sedimentation takes place; lower down the chances of fossilisation increase but there is also a greater likelihood of the river itself damaging the thanatocoenosis.

The evaporites of springs can be regarded as a special type of running water sediment. The circumstances in which these deposits are formed give a special character to the thanatocoenosis. The rapid consolidation of the sediment greatly restricts transport. It would not, however, be correct to equate biocoenosis and thanatocoenosis in this instance; firstly because by no means all of the autochthonous organisms are susceptible to fossilisation; and secondly because a considerable influx of exotic elements takes place, particularly from the air. Most thanatocoenoses in this type of deposit therefore contain the remains of plants, especially leaves, from the surrounding areas. Deposits of this type are limited in extent and of infrequent occurrence because they are continental deposits which are thus prone to later erosion. These thanatocoenoses are important, however, as they usually contain elements such as land or freshwater molluscs and plants which do not often occur as fossils elsewhere.

Thanatocoenoses in still-water sediments are classified as lacustrine or paludal, according to whether they originate in lakes or swamps. The two types cannot always be sharply distinguished, and there are transitional phases and areas. The total image of a lake depends on its size, its bathymetric, physical, chemical, biological and climatological conditions. Since each of these factors can vary enormously, the number of types of lake is very great, and the number of possible lacustrine sediment types and thanatocoenoses is consequently very large. Exhaustive study of all the many possibilities lies beyond the scope of this work, particularly as lacustrine sediments account for a very small proportion of sedimentary rocks. It should be noted, however, that many present-day lakes have been thoroughly investigated and thus form a good basis for the study of fossil lakes which are particularly common in Pleistocene deposits. As will be seen later, there is a certain correspondence between lacustrine and marine thanatocoenoses, the latter being geologically the more important. A thorough study of recent and fossil lacustrine thanatocoenoses will therefore make a valuable contribution to a better understanding of marine thanatocoenoses.

Without going into details about lacustrine conditions, lacustrine thanatocoenoses can be divided into three groups: the strand-line zone, the shell zone and the lake bed in the narrower sense. As the mechanical forces in lakes are generally small, there being no tides, the strand-line zone at the highest water mark consists of fine and light material. It is a typical allochthonous thanatocoenosis, in which purely land elements, such as plants and animals, usually predominate. Obviously a thanatocoenosis of this type dependent, in each case, on the prevailing circumstances, can vary enormously. There is little chance of a lacustrine thanatocoenosis, like a fluvial one, being finally buried by sediment.

The shell zone is a very characteristic element in many recent and fossil lacustrine environments. Numerous Pleistocene lacustrine sediments have a well-developed shell zone. It consists of a strip, often not more than a few metres wide, at the place where the incoming waves and the backwash meet. This zone generally lies in water which is not more than two metres deep. Under certain bathymetric and hydrological conditions, however, shell zones may occur in deeper water as a result of currents influenced by differences in density. These differences are in turn caused by differences in the temperature of the water. As with the strand-line zone, the shell zone is an allochthonous thanatocoenosis but consists of lacustrine elements. The factors which determine sedimentation on lake beds are so numerous and varied that lacustrine sediments range from purely clastic at one end of the scale to purely organic at the other. The factors which determine a lacustrine thanatocoenosis are almost as numerous. Consequently, the thanatocoenoses of lacustrine deposits also display an extraordinarily varied pattern which cannot be reduced to a common denominator. In general, autochthonous benthonic elements are in the minority. Nektonic and planktonic forms predominate, while among the finer components, such as pollen and spores, there are many which sank after transportation by wind. For more detailed study, Twenhofel (1950, pp. 84-89) and limnological literature may be referred to.

The greater part of all thanatocoenoses is of marine origin. A large number of factors determine the final pattern of marine thanatocoenoses which are as varied as marine environments. The composition of the marine thanatocoenosis is primarily dependent on the local flora and fauna which in turn are the result of the interaction of countless factors—physical, chemical and biological. In thanatocoenoses which are purely autochthonous and therefore benthonic, the pattern of the biocoenosis at a given locality, together with the fossilisation conditions, determine the pattern of the thanatocoenosis. Autochthonous marine thanatocoenoses are rare; apart from the many types of reefs, the category includes thanatocoenoses of brachiopods and lamellibranchs. They are nearly always associated with shallow water, otherwise there is a strong possibility of allochthonous elements being added.

Most marine thanatocoenoses are, therefore, allochthonous or are of a mixed character in which allochthonous elements generally predominate. The degree of autochthony varies considerably and this must be allowed for in ecological analysis of a thanatocoenosis; in addition to the pattern of movement of the environment, which is partially reflected in the sediment, the ecological character of the component elements of the thanatocoenosis should also be taken into account. Craig's palaeoecological analysis of the Top Hosie shale (Lower Carboniferous, Scotland) forms an excellent example. He observed a change which takes place in palaeontological aspect within a thin layer (0·60 m) from autochthonous to principally

PLATE 3

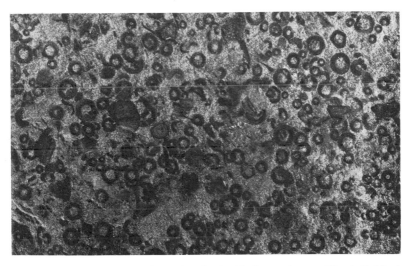

Concentration of single columnals of crinoids in sandstone. The individual ossicles lie flat on the bedding plane. Actual size. Ordovician, Shropshire.

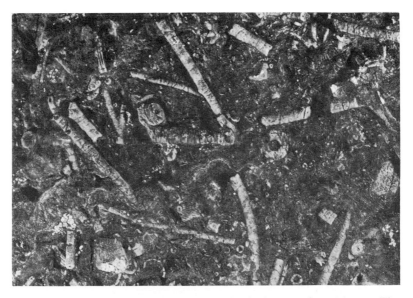

Autochthonous occurrence of fragments of crinoid stems in sandstone. The fragments and a few individual ossicles lie flat in the bedding plane. The stem fragments show no definite orientation. Actual size. La Vid Limestone, Lower Devonian, Cantabrian Mountains.

PLATE 4

Concentration of gastropod shells of the same species but different dimensions. 2/3 actual size. Eocene freshwater limestone. Verzenay (Marne).

Concentration of badly graded elements in a reef talus (corals, bryozoans, crinoids and brachiopods). 3/5 actual size. Wenlock Limestone, Silurian, Shropshire.

allochthonous elements, and noted that it is coupled with a palpable increase in grain size in the sediment (Fig. 21).

For a general survey, marine thanatocoenoses are best arranged according to their bathymetric conditions. The typical accumulations of pelagic radiolarians and globigerinids in abyssal thanatocoenoses are almost unknown outside present-day ocean basins. They are examples of purely allochthonous thanatocoenoses, all component elements of which have undergone at least one, and in this case considerable, vertical movement.

Bathyal thanatocoenoses are also known from the present oceans. They are relatively scarce, however, in older sediments. The deepest of the ammonite thanatocoenoses from the Cretaceous of Texas and Mexico described by G. Scott certainly belong to this zone (Fig. 22). According to Scott the thick, smooth ammonites (*Lytoceras, Phylloceras*) are characteristic of these sediments formed below the 200-metre limit. The same probably applies to the similar ammonites from Alpine localities described by Haug and Kilian, although it remains to be seen how far more recent ideas about the infilling of this type of trough conflict with earlier gene-

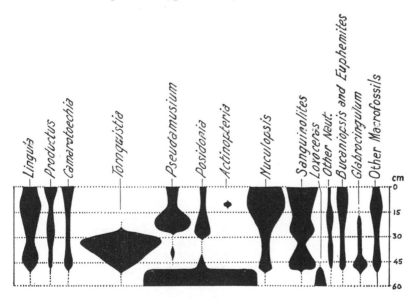

Fig. 21.   Quantitative composition of the macrofauna of Top Hosie shale. Lower Carboniferous, Scotland.) After Craig.

5

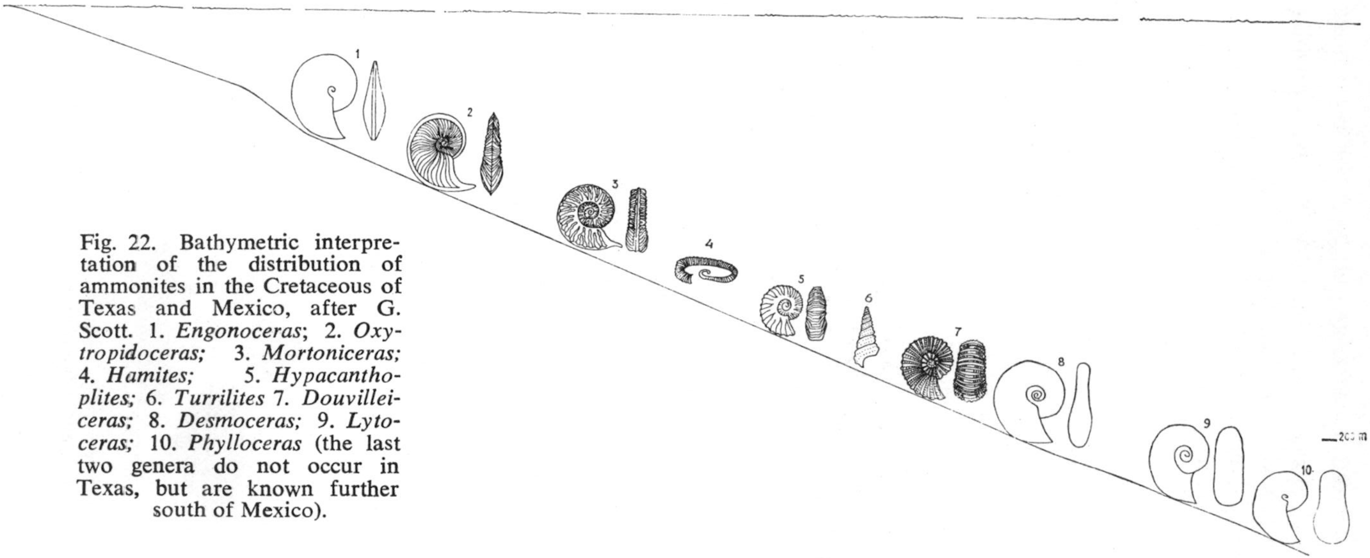

Fig. 22. Bathymetric interpretation of the distribution of ammonites in the Cretaceous of Texas and Mexico, after G. Scott. 1. *Engonoceras*; 2. *Oxytropidoceras*; 3. *Mortoniceras*; 4. *Hamites*; 5. *Hypacanthoplites*; 6. *Turrilites* 7. *Douvilleiceras*; 8. *Desmoceras*; 9. *Lytoceras*; 10. *Phylloceras* (the last two genera do not occur in Texas, but are known further south of Mexico).

rally held views. Naturally bathyal thanatocoenoses are particularly likely to be encountered in geosynclinal sediments, although even there they are restricted to incidental cases.

By far the greater part of all marine thanatocoenoses, both in geosynclinal and epicontinental sedimentary successions, originates in the sublittoral zone. The transport factor must be added to the large number of variable factors influencing the biocoenoses in this zone. Its influence usually increases towards the shore. Beach thanatocoenoses, of which remarkably few fossil examples are known, can generally be regarded as completely allochthonous.

In spite of the obvious influence of transport, seen from the gradation and orientation of the material, the importance of this factor should not be exaggerated. From observations made by Wasmund and others in the Baltic (probably one of the best investigated areas in this respect) it appears that benthonic elements in beach thanatocoenoses live for the most part above a depth of 12 metres. Elements from deeper water are only sporadically encountered and benthonic organisms whose habitat is below a depth of 20 metres do not occur as a rule in beach thanatocoenoses.

The mixing of material from different bathymetric zones is not serious enough to inhibit the drawing of palaeoecological conclusions. This is already apparent from G. Scott's investigations into the distribution of ammonites in the Cretaceous of Texas and Mexico. The existence of obvious zones in the distribution of various species deprives transport of its importance—rather a surprising conclusion in a group such as the ammonites where considerable transport of empty shells is readily assumed in order to explain their usefulness as index fossils. If Scott's research provides an example of the horizontal sequence of bathymetric zones, Elias's work on the distribution of various fossils in the uppermost Permian of Kansas, the so-called Big Blue, furnishes an example of a vertical sequence with characteristic fossils from different bathymetric zones, resulting from the fairly regular fluctuations in sea level. These fluctuations are also reflected in the rhythmic pattern of the sedimentation (Fig. 23).

Although transport is certainly responsible for many concentrations of fossils, it would be incorrect to assume that it causes every such accumulation. Parker's work along the eastern side of the Mississippi delta shows that a concentration of fossils can also be the result of the absence of normal sedimentation. In such cases the sediment formed consists almost entirely of the remains of organisms. A. H. Müller had already come to the conclusion that accumulations of shells ("Muschelplaster") in the German Muschelkalk (middle marine part of the Germanic facies of the Trias) were indications of interrupted sedimentation. Conversely, extremely rapid sedimentation (along the eastern part of the Mississippi delta it can be as much as 0·50 metres per year) may cause fossils to be very sparsely distributed in the sediment.

The allochthonous concentrations of fossils in certain layers that frequently occur in sublittoral deposits can generally be satisfactorily explained either by transport or by interruptions in sedimentation. It is rarely necessary to ascribe them to some sudden and massive death, as was often done in the earlier literature. On the other hand, this factor is frequently involved in autochthonous thanatocoenoses.

Littoral thanatocoenoses which occur between the high and low water marks form a special case within the shallow-water zone.

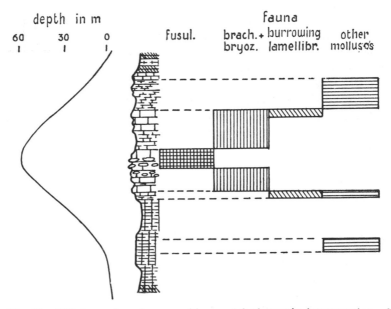

Fig. 23. Lithology, faunal composition and bathymetric interpretation of one sedimentation cycle from the Permian of Kansas. After Elias.

They vary considerably in pattern according to the morphological condition of the coast. The extremes are represented by the thanatocoenoses of rocky coasts whose fossil examples are very rarely encountered, and by those of tidal flats from which type of coast various fossil examples are known. Littoral thanatocoenoses are usually characterised by the appearance of marine and continental elements together. Areas with littoral sedimentation, such as mudflats and tidal marshes, are distinguished from most other marine sediments by the frequency of autochthonous thanatocoenoses—a result of the comparative tranquility which is a feature of such regions.

There is a still more striking mingling of continental and marine organisms in river estuaries and deltas through the fluvial transport of the remains of land and freshwater organisms and also because of the existence of belts of different salinity with different organisms. Many marine organisms penetrate to the polyhaline zone, while conversely many freshwater organisms which possess a certain adaptability to an increased chlorine ion concentration are able to live in the oligohaline zone. The intermediate mesohaline zone, the true brackish water area, has its own characteristic flora and fauna. The geological pattern is an important factor in the recognition of fossil thanatocoenoses in these transitional areas.

6. Systematic palaeoecology

Introduction Palaeoecology is such a young branch of palaeontology that it is too early to be able to give anything resembling a complete picture of the ecology of fossil organisms. The following notes are only intended to give an impression of the possibilities and difficulties of palaeoecological research by means of a few comparatively random examples.

Foraminifera Recent foraminifers inhabit the sea from the high water mark to a depth of 1000 metres and sometimes much more. Most forms are benthonic, especially in the shallow seas where they occur both in the vagrant and in the sessile benthos. Sessile benthonic species are generally attached to plants or other objects on the sea-bed. Only sessile species inhabit the littoral zone and are characterised by small and rather thin shells. The species of the sublittoral zone generally have larger and thicker shells, usually in the form of a disk or flat spiral. As dead specimens of foraminifers from both zones are easily mixed, the occurrence of littoral and sublittoral types together in fossil sediments can sometimes be taken as an indication of the proximity of the former coastline, assuming that the same relationship between the form and structure of the shell, and the environment has always existed. It is known that various species from genera inhabiting the littoral zone and the higher parts of the sublittoral zone can tolerate brackish water.

(*Quinqueloculina fusca* lives exclusively in brackish water in which the salinity may drop to as little as one part per thousand. The presence of this species in fossile foraminiferal faunas, the remainder of which consist of marine forms with a toleration of brackish water, can therefore be regarded as an indication of a brackish environment (Hedberg, 1934).)

In certain genera planktonic species occur which may form an important component of sediments by reason of the abundance of their individuals. The sedimentary pattern of large parts of the present ocean floor is dominated by empty globigerinid shells. Inspired by the discovery of these sediments by the oceanographic expeditions of the second half of the last century, palaeontologists were inclined to consider the chalk facies of the Upper Cretaceous which is sometimes rich in foraminifers as a fossil example of this phenomenon. L. Cayeux, however, showed the untenability of this view because the depth of water in which these sediments originated scarcely exceeded that of the sublittoral zone. Recent examples of this type of sediment are rare, and, on the scale in which they occur in the Cretaceous, quite unknown.

The shells of foraminifers are easily transported over large distances because of their small dimensions. In many deposits foraminifers show obvious traces of selection during transport and sedimentation. As many foraminifers serve as food for other marine organisms, their shells apparently passing through the intestinal canal without much damage, this possible mode of transport should also perhaps be taken into account when considering fossil foraminifers.

Although their palaeoecological significance is generally recognised, few quantitative investigations have been carried out which give a clear insight into the influence of the environment (such as salinity and depth) on the distribution of foraminifers.

Radiolaria Like the foraminifers, radiolarians are marine organisms with a very great horizontal and vertical distribution in all seas. Radiolarians are, however, exclusively pelagic and planktonic, a circumstance which assists their horizontal distribution. Recent deposits with an abundance of radiolarians are confined to the deepest parts of the oceans, below 4000 metres. Radiolarians also occur in the sediments of higher zones, but they then generally disappear under the preponderance of other sedimentary components.

Fossil radiolarians are known from sediments of widely differing ages. Where radiolarian shells form an appreciable part of the sedimentary material, they are regarded as an indication of deep water. This may be correct in some instances, but this certainly does not apply to the majority of sediments with radiolarians. In most cases geological circumstances and the character of the sediments above and below exclude the possibility of a deep-water origin. It is probable that, to a large degree, other factors than depth alone influence the formation of sediments rich in radiolarians, factors such as the silica content of the water and the scarcity of other material for sedimentation.

Many genera of radiolarians are widely distributed with various species in different environments, so that in fossil material the systematic position of the species encountered provides little information regarding environmental conditions. For this the shell is perhaps more important. It appears that forms inhabiting the upper layers of water possess larger and more lightly built shells than the deep-water forms. The latter will naturally be restricted to deep-water sediments, but the former may also be deposited there.

Porifera With a few exceptions belonging to the family Spongillidae, all sponges are sessile benthonic marine organisms. Recent forms are found from the littoral zone to more than 6000 metres in depth, and from tropical to arctic waters.

Calcispongea are for the most part inhabitants of the shallow seas, and many species of this class live in the littoral zone. Lithistid sponges, the largest group of the Demospongea, occur in the deeper parts of the sublittoral zone and in the highest parts of the bathyal zone, between approximately 100 and 400 metres. The Hyalospongea (Hexactinellida) live mainly in the bathyal and abyssal zones. At present their main distribution lies between 200 and 500 metres, but geological data seems to indicate that formerly this group had many representatives in the sublittoral zone (see Section 7).

The sessile mode of life of the sponges creates favourable conditions for autochthonous fossils. On the other hand their skeletal structure which in many spunges consists of loose elements leads to complete disintegration after death. Fossil deposits are known from various localities consisting for the greater part of such loose skeletal components.

Sponges are sometimes found in association with corals and other organisms that produce organic structures in sediments; they also appear in many coral reefs. Sponges may cause the growth of organic structures quite independently, as for example in the Upper Jurassic of southern Germany. Roll (1934) showed that the environmental relationship of these organic structures is quite different from that of coral reefs. The sponges, unlike the corals, were not able to raise themselves above the surface of the sediment and formed a flat slab level with the sea-bed. Only the considerable amount of sediment and the ability of the sponges beneath the living upper layer to trap the sediment enabled the sponge colony to grow upwards, thus keeping pace with the sedimentation around it.

Such sponge biostromes display a remarkable poverty in other organisms. This is probably connected with the fact that they did not provide a suitable substratum for sessile organisms since their featureless surface offered no protection to vagrant organisms and they were not in demand as food.

Coelenterata Recent coelenterates are for the most part marine animals, while the plentiful fossil species known were exclusively marine. Fossil coelenterates are very unevenly distributed over the different groups. Groups without hard parts are hardly known as fossils, with the exception of a few Siphonophorida, because they naturally have poor chances of fossilisation. On the other hand certain groups, such as Stromatoporoidea, Rugosa and Tabulata, are very important palaeontologically, but have no representatives among recent fauna. The ecological conditions in which these animals lived can, therefore, only be deduced by analogy with recent coelenterates, and from the geological circumstances of their occurrence.

The most important group which embraces both fossil and recent species is the order Scleractinia. Practically all post-Palaeozoic and living corals belong to this order which is the obvious starting point for an ecological discussion of the coelenterates.

Part of the Scleractinia live in symbiosis with dinoflagellates and appear as reef-builders on a large scale. Their ecological requirements are apparently determined in part by those of the dinoflagellates. The greatest depth at which these hermatypic corals live is roughly 90 metres, but the reef-building species all live at depths of less than 50 metres. The lower limit of their optimum conditions lies still higher, at about 30 metres. This is almost certainly connected with the need of light for photosynthesis by the dinoflagellates. The best temperatures for the hermatypic Scleractinia lie between 25° and 29°C, although many species can tolerate lower temperatures for a certain time.

Corals are carnivorous, feeding mainly on tiny planktonic creatures. Continual movement of the water is necessary to supply the sessile corals with their food. The same water movement prevents over-sedimentation, a condition to which scleractinic corals, unlike sponges and, perhaps, stromatoporoids, are very sensitive. A normal sediment, consisting of fine sand or still finer grained particles, does not provide a suitable substratum for corals to attach themselves to. If there is no firm rock-bed, objects such as stones, or skeletons and shells of other sessile organisms are necessary.

The ahermatypic Scleractinia do not live in symbiosis with dinoflagellates, and, probably as a result of this, are much less restricted in their choice of environment. Recent representatives are found to a depth of 6000 metres, but most species live between 200 and 500 metres. From this it follows that the thermal conditions of their environment must also be different. Their optimum temperature lies between 5° and 10°C, but a number of species can tolerate temperatures only just above freezing point. They form colonies, but do not build reefs in the proper sense of the word.

Hermatypic corals are found in the tropical and subtropical belt, between 35°N and 32°S, but the reef-building species have a rather more restricted distribution. Ahermatypic corals on the other

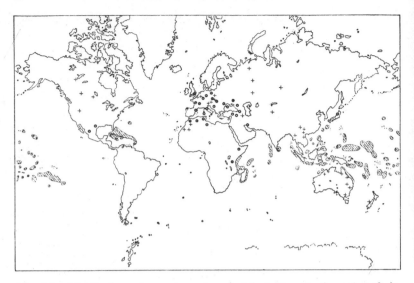

Fig. 24. Distribution of recent coral reefs (shaded), and of coral reefs in the Jurassic (circles) and in the Middle Devonian (crosses). After Joleaud, Hill and other data.

hand are found throughout a much wider area, from 70°N (between Norway and Iceland) to 75°S (the Ross Sea).

Hermatypic Scleractinia are the most important reef-building coelenterates of the present time and have been so since their first appearance in the Middle Trias. The reef-building capacities of the Scleractinia are considerably greater than those of the Palaeozoic corals, probably as a result of (i) the porous structure of their corallium and (ii) the symbiosis with dinoflagellates, an important source of oxygen which has a stimulating effect on their metabolism. It should not be forgotten that various other groups of organisms contribute considerably to the growth of the reef, sometimes even surpassing the corals as builders.

As the symbiosis with the dinoflagellates is not obviously reflected in the hard parts and appears not to be a characteristic of particular families, it has not been established whether this symbiosis has had its present significance throughout the whole history of the coelenterates in question. It is possible that this symbiosis has gradually developed since the Middle Trias. The reefs of the

Mesozoic are not of the same magnitude as recent and Pleistocene reefs. Geological evidence, however, indicates that the Mesozoic reefs developed mainly under similar ecological conditions to the present reefs.

The most important Palaeozoic coelenterate groups were the Rugosa (Tetracorallia), the Tabulata and the Stromatoporoidea. All three are extinct groups of which the phylogenetic relationships, and in consequence the systematic position, are not clear. A comparison with recent relatives offers little firm ground on which to base a reconstruction of the ecological circumstances in which these groups lived. For this geological conditions, deduced from the surrounding sediment, have to be referred to and it is not surprising therefore that many points in the ecology of these extinct groups remain unclarified.

Tabulata and Stromatoporoidea are the most important builders of many Palaeozoic reefs. Rugosa generally play a minor part. Although Palaeozoic reefs are usually compared with recent structures, there are a number of important differences. Their dimensions are much smaller than those of recent reefs; no known Palaeozoic reef can be compared, for example, with the Great Barrier Reef of Australia. There is much less variety of component species in Palaeozoic reefs; and many also lack the obvious differences in a horizontal direction which are so characteristic of many recent reefs.

Tabulata and Stromatoporoidea appear in general to be mutually exclusive in the Palaeozoic reefs. Stromatoporoidea are generally absent, or only represented by a few particular types, in reefs where Tabulata are preponderant. Conversely typical stromatoporoid reefs are known where tabulate corals are almost entirely lacking. This might indicate that the ecological demands of the two groups were so similar that they could not be mutually tolerant. It is more likely, however, that their demands differed so greatly that an environment which suited one was generally unfavourable for the other. The alternation of Stromatoporoidea with other Coelenterata in certain Devonian reefs of the Ardennes can be explained by assuming that the Stromatoporoidea represent phases of reduced depth of water. This does not mean that the Stromatoporoidea occurred exclusively in very shallow water. Massive types sometimes alternate with more delicately built forms. The latter often occur with brachiopods and crinoids and could be an indication of slightly deeper water. Apart from bathymetric considerations, other factors would have influenced the inter-relation of Stromatoporoidea and Tabulata. The conditions in which Stromatoporoidea are often found makes it probable that they were less sensitive to the influence of sedimentation than most other colonial coelenterates.

A frequent subject of discussion is the extent to which the environmental requirements of recent reef-building corals, especially with regard to temperature and depth, are applicable to Palaeozoic reefs (Fig. 24). Although there is a tendency to assume a similarity without critical examination, particularly in geological literature, there is insufficient evidence for such a generalisation. Too little is known at present about the relationships between the metabolism, the structure of the hard parts and the ecological requirements of the Palaeozoic coelenterates. It has already been seen that in Scleractinia the depth at which they occur is limited by the requirements of the dinoflagellates with which they live in symbiosis. As far as is known, Palaeozoic reefs did not have this symbiosis. There are, however, many Palaeozoic reefs known where the total pattern of geological conditions indicates comparatively shallow water. This conclusion finds a certain measure of support in the occurrence of solitary corals in the Palaeozoic in circumstances that indicate a greater depth of water. It would be incorrect, however, to infer from this that all Palaeozoic reefs grew at a depth of less than 50 metres.

The same applies, *mutatis mutandis*, for temperature. Many Palaeozoic reefs certainly give reason for supposing that warm seas were necessary for their full development. Results of recent palaeomagnetic studies seem to indicate that the position of the equator relative to the present position of the continents has shifted considerably in the course of the Earth's history and that most of the organic reefs known from the geological record developed in the tropical belt. Much more research will be needed, however, before all the problems regarding the palaeoecological relationships of Palaeozoic coelenterates can be satisfactorily solved.

Bryozoa Although fossil Bryozoa are perhaps best known as inhabitants of various sorts of reefs, their ecological possibilities are much greater. Recent bryozoans live in both salt- and fresh-water, but of the numerous fossil species there is none which can be regarded with certainty as a freshwater form. This must certainly be due to the poor chances of fossilisation of freshwater species.

All Bryozoa are sessile animals which live in colonies, attached to the sea-bed or to other organisms or objects. The form of the colonies varies greatly. There are wide-branched, rather plant-like forms, and there are many bryozoans that form an enclosing crust over other objects. The former soon break off and are then easily transported, while the latter are often transported with the encrusted object. In spite of their sessile mode of life, bryozoans do not have the same significance as autochthonous fossils as some other groups of sessile organisms.

Bryozoans display a wide distribution in different bathymetric zones. Recent bryozoans show a definite preference for sea beds with carbonate or clay sedimentation. From the fact that fossil bryozoans seldom occur in sandy sediments it may be inferred that in this respect their environmental requirements were roughly the same. The abundance of bryozoans in some sandy Pliocene sediments of the North Sea basin is rather remarkable in this light. The English Coralline Crag even owes its name to the numerous remains of bryozoans. If it is assumed that these are allochthonous, there remains the question of in which area of different sedimentary type they originated.

Bryozoa are plentiful in all types of reef. They have usually had a comparatively modest share in the building of the reef, particularly in comparison with the more substantial contribution of various coelenterates. The extent, however, of the bryozoan over-growth that many reefs must have had is apparent from their share in the flank sediments of such structures. Fragments of bryozoan colonies together with broken off pieces of coral and the stems of crinoids are characteristic components of the flank sediments of Palaeozoic and later reefs (Plate 4, facing p. 57).

Bryozoans sometimes appear as the most important contributors to reefs, not only before the corals partially took over this role in the Upper Silurian, but for a long time afterwards. Typical bryozoan reefs are known from the Cainozoic of the Paratethys, and also from the Permian (the Zechstein of Thuringia and Durham).

Brachiopoda   Recent brachiopods only faintly reflect the former extent of this group. Many types of Palaeozoic brachiopods have no comparable counterparts in recent fauna. In isolation, the fact that all recent brachiopods are marine animals implies little regarding the environment of the much more numerous fossil species, but there is nevertheless good reason for assuming that the group has been exclusively marine throughout its long history. A few recent species, such as *Lingula*, tolerate brackish water, and the geological conditions in which fossil representatives of this genus are sometimes encountered indicate that it already possessed a certain tolerance of reduced salinity in the Palaeozoic. The same is perhaps true for a few other genera.

The bathymetric conditions in which the few recent brachiopods live are widely divergent. Of the approximately 200 recent species known, roughly a third live exclusively in water less than 200 metres deep, a third in deeper water, to 6000 metres, and a third occurs both in the littoral zone and at great depth. Different brachiopod species thus have a very large bathymetric distribution. As far as is known at present, no close connection exists between the bathymetric conditions and the systematic position of the brachiopods. Even if this did exist in recent groups, it would still have little significance with regard to the many extinct families. It would therefore appear that, with a few exceptions, such as *Lingula*, brachiopods by themselves are of little use in the reconstruction of the bathymetric conditions in which fossil species lived. Not until the relationships between the ecology of both recent and fossil brachiopods, and geological conditions of the sedimentation have been much more systematically examined than has hitherto been the case can a better evaluation of brachiopods be expected bathymetrically. In such an investigation attention should also be given to the relationship between the shell form and the conditions of the organism's life, as these are obviously connected in some recent brachiopods. *Terebratalia obsoleta* displays a short, compact shell form in individuals that live in waters where there is considerable movement, while in calmer waters the shell has a more Spirifer-like form.

The same difficulties which arise in ascertaining the bathymetric circumstances of brachiopods are encountered with regard to the thermal conditions. Recent brachiopods live in both arctic and tropical seas, and many species have a wide thermal distribution. It is reasonable to assume that a genus such as *Lingula* has always lived in the warmer seas, but there is otherwise little known about the thermal factor in the distribution of fossil brachiopods.

Most brachiopods, after a short free-living stage, lead a sessile existence. They are usually attached to the substratum by means of a pedicle, sometimes directly through one of the valves, generally the pedicle valve. The latter is the case in *Prorichthofenia* where the pedicle valve assumes a conical form, while the other valve is reduced to a sort of small lid. Such types occupy the same place among the brachiopods as the rudists among the lamellibranchs.

In some cases the pedicle may be lost during the life cycle, and such species lie unattached on the sea-bed. Strong lateral growth together with a small dorso-ventral development (a flattening of the shell, observed in Palaeozoic strophomenids) is often regarded as an adaptation to this specialised benthonic mode of life. Only a few brachiopods, such as *Lingula*, live buried in the sea-bed.

Brachiopods sometimes occur packed tightly together in large numbers, fastened into a coherent mass by their spines. Such cases are described as brachiopod reefs.

Fossil brachiopods are encountered in clayey and sandy sediments as well as in limestones. Little is known for certain about the brachiopods' preference for, or tolerance of, particular bottom conditions. Typically autochthonous finds come principally from limestones, where they sometimes form the reef-like concentrations mentioned above, as in the Permian of Texas and the Muschelkalk of Germany, while many brachiopods are a normal concomitant in all types of reefs. Fossil brachiopods in general may have had the ability to adapt to divergent bottom conditions. The spines with which the valves of various brachiopods are equipped may perhaps have served the function of raising the animals a little above the sea-bed, protecting them from the harmful consequences of a benthonic mode of life in areas of active sedimentation (Fig. 25).

Mollusca The molluscs form such a large, and morphologically and ecologically varied group that the three most important classes (Lamellibranchia, Gastropoda and Cephalopoda) require separate consideration.

The lamellibranchs are aquatic animals, with the exception of certain species of the family Sphaeridae which live on land between damp leaves. They inhabit salt, brackish and fresh water. The bathymetric distribution of the marine species is very large. The shallow seas are in many localities thickly populated, almost to the high water mark, with lamellibranchs, but other species live to a considerable depth in the bathyal and abyssal zones. Recent lamellibranchs have been discovered in the Mindano Trench at a depth of more than 10,000 metres. Freshwater species occur at more than 1000 metres above sea-level. Geographical distribution is also extensive in this group which thus displays considerable adaptability both with regard to depth and to temperature.

In other respects the lamellibranchs possess limited ecological possibilities; they are benthonic and feed by filtering the usable elements from the large quantities of material that passes through their digestive tracts. As benthonic animals the lamellibranchs exhibit widely divergent adaptations—sessile, vagrant and burrowing forms are encountered. Each of these three groups displays a fairly obvious connection between the mode of life and the form of the shell. In sessile forms symmetry is usually lost, particularly in species which are attached to the substratum not by byssal

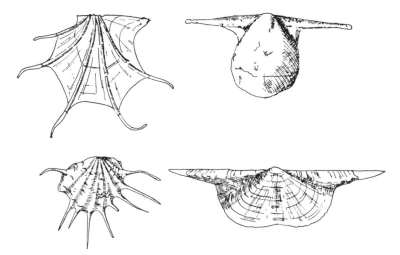

Fig. 25. *Above*: lamellibranchs, *Avicula* and *Actinodesma; below*: brachiopods *Atrypa* and *Productus* with elongated spines or hinge line. After Dacqué.

threads but directly by the shell. This tendency is not pronounced in oyster valves, but is clearer in fossil genera such as *Exogyra* and *Gryphaea* and assumes extreme forms in the extinct group of the rudists.

Lamellibranchs that live freely on the sea-bed are usually characterised by flattened valves, the result of a reduction of the dimensions transversely through the plane of symmetry in relation to height and length (*Pecten*). The position of the animal is rotated, so that the plane of symmetry comes to lie roughly horizontally. These two phenomena also appear in other groups of vagrant benthonic animals.

Burrowing species often exhibit marked longitudinal development; the recent *Solen* is an extreme example. It occurs in less extreme forms in many other genera, fossil and recent. Species which live buried in the sea-bed often have gaping valves.

As indicators of temperature, lamellibranchs have little value. Large, thick-shelled forms, such as those of *Tridacna* and among the rudists, are characteristic of warm seas. Many marine species, particularly from the littoral zone, can live in water of low salinity. Brackish-water forms are sometimes distinguished by smaller and thinner shells. As it is probable that the same reaction to reduced salinity existed in fossil species, the appearance of these two forms of the same species side by side in older sediments can provide a valuable indication of brackish water conditions. Conversely there are freshwater forms that are tolerant of a certain degree of salinity; physiologically this is even easier to understand.

Species that are still extant occur in some Cainozoic deposits and often provide a reliable indication of the palaeoecological circumstances. It is difficult or even impossible to reach trustworthy conclusions where such species are absent. Only rarely do the ecological and systematic boundaries coincide. The family of the Unionidae is an example of a systematic unit, all the members of which live exclusively in fresh water. In older sediments, where the link with recent species is generally lacking, uncertainties remain. This is the case with the so-called non-marine lamellibranchs of the Carboniferous (*Carbonicola* and related genera). In spite of numerous discoveries and much data concerning the environment, it has never been established whether these were fresh- or brackish-water animals. The shells of *Carbonicola* are undeniably reminiscent of those of recent freshwater species but evidence from other groups with which they sometimes occur makes it doubtful whether they were exclusively freshwater.

Lamellibranchs seldom furnish directly reliable evidence about bathymetric conditions. Species which live in the surf zone often display adaptation to its mechanical requirements but caution is necessary when advancing this as a characteristic.

Marine species sometimes occur in enormous, tightly packed agglomerations. Fossil examples of this are known from deposits of different ages.

Among all the large systematic units of the animal kingdom, few show such a great development in their ecological possibilities as the gastropods. Not only do they inhabit the sea from the high water mark to a depth of more than 5000 metres, all types of fresh water and the land, but they are equally diverse in their modes of life. There are herbivores, carrion eaters and predators among the gastropods, sessile and vagrant benthonic, and nektonic species. In spite of this great diversity of environment and mode of life, most recent gastropods appear to be herbivorous and to inhabit shallow warm seas.

The palaeoecological interpretation of fossil gastropod faunas presents the same difficulties as are encountered with the lamellibranchs. The systematic position of gastropods does not always give an explanation of the conditions in which they lived. Many families contain exclusively marine species, but others, such as the Neritidae have marine as well as freshwater and land species. The whole subclass of the Pulmonata which breathe not through gills but by means of a type of lung consists entirely of freshwater and land-inhabiting forms, but unfortunately the systematic position of some genera that are known only as fossils is doubtful. The systematic classification of gastropods is based entirely on soft parts, and there appears to be no close relationship between these and the shell. In many Cainozoic deposits in which comparisons can be made with recent species gastropods provide usable indicators of the environment. This applies both to marine and freshwater environments. Gastropods enter brackish-water environments both from the sea and from fresh water.

Other families besides the Pulmonata have exclusively freshwater forms, such as the Paludinidae, or fresh- and brackish-water forms, such as the Hydrobiidae. The species belonging to these groups are distinguished from many marine, especially neritic, forms by their very thin shells.

In contrast to the two previous classes of Mollusca, the approximately 400 recent species of Cephalopoda are all marine, and there are good reasons for assuming that the more than 10,000 known fossil species were also exclusively marine animals. In spite of the great geological importance of the cephalopods, reflected in a vast quantity of stratigraphical and systematic publications, the palaeoecology of this class is not yet adequately known.

The three or four recent species of the genus *Nautilus* form the only real starting point for the palaeoecology of the thousands of fossil species of Nautiloidea and Ammonoidea, and even this point of contact is of limited usefulness, since it is improbable that the ecological conditions of these last survivors of two very extensive subclasses are representative of those in which the fossil groups flourished. On analogy with many other extensive groups with a wide distribution, it is probable that the Nautiloidea and Ammonoidea formerly showed great variation in their ecological adaptability, although there is little reliable data and much contradictory evidence on the mode of life of these two groups.

Recent *Nautilus* species live principally between depths of 500 to 700 metres, although occasionally specimens have been caught in shallower waters. They are excellent swimmers, propelling themselves rapidly by forcing water through the funnel. The well-known reconstructions of fossil Nautiloidea (and Ammonoidea), in which the animals crawl on their tentacles over the sea-bed, are not supported by what is known of the recent *Nautilus*. In this connection it is important to remember that no fossil tracks of these animals are known.

The first palaeoecological question that arises is whether there were truly benthonic forms among the fossil Nautiloidea and Ammonoidea. In spite of the negative evidence already referred to, it is generally assumed that some of the ammonites were benthonic. A curved rostrum, by which the aperture is raised above the sediment, is often associated with a benthonic mode of life, as is an asymmetrical development of the suture lines and the colour pattern. In the first case the shell would have had a vertical, in the second a horizontal position, which could perhaps be effected with regard to hydrostatic equilibrium in forms where the body-chamber occupies exactly one whorl. From many ammonite studies there appears a certain connection between the shell form and the character of the sediment, but when an attempt to generalise from this is made the data often proves to be contradictory. Many ammonites were perhaps not benthonic in the strict sense but lived in the protection of a benthonic flora. In particular, species with ornamented, less streamlined shells lived in this manner. Smooth, slender, discoidal forms may be regarded as a successful adaptation to a free-swimming mode of life: nektonic species particularly figure in this category.

Little is known with certainty about the depth at which Nautiloidea and Ammonoidea lived. Ammonites are only rarely encountered in reefs and in coarser clastic sediments, and then usually in damaged condition. Very shallow seas apparently did not provide an environment in which ammonites preferred to live. The question of whether ammonites could live at great depths or were associated with particular bathymetric zones is linked with the problem of to what extent their shells were able to withstand high and great variations in water pressures. If the small chambers behind the body-chamber were filled with gas, as in the recent *Nautilus* species, it must be assumed that the gas pressure was different in different species according to the depth at which they lived. If there were species which could live at various depths, it would seem necessary to assume that they were able to vary the gas pressure according to circumstances, although ribs on the shell, and the greatest possible length of attachment of the septa to the shell wall could have contributed to greater solidity. Complex suture lines are implied here and Arkell suggested that these might indicate a nektonic mode of life in deep water, while simple suture lines would point to shallow water or fairly inactive swimmers. In this connection it should be noted that the Lytoceratidae and the Phylloceratidae with their very complicated suture lines have long been considered deep-water forms. It is possible that the great breadth of the whorls in these groups is also associated with a deep water mode of life. It is not known whether the recent *Nautilus* species are able to vary the gas pressure according to need, although these animals are able to survive great differences of depth and pressure: they can descend to a depth of approximately 1000 metres, corresponding to a difference of pressure of 100 kg/cm².

Much more analytical research into ammonite faunas in relation to the remaining faunas and the sedimentary pattern will be needed for a better understanding of the ecological conditions in which ammonites lived. The same applies, *mutatis mutandis*, to the Nautiloidea.

Rather more is known about Coleoidea (Dibranchiata), which are represented in recent fauna by a good number of species, but it would be rash to assume that knowledge of the palaeoecology of this group is therefore complete. Like the recent species, most of the fossil species were good swimmers. It may be assumed from the conditions in which fossil remains occur that some of the fossil species inhabited shallow seas while others lived in deeper waters. It has not yet been established whether there were ben-thonic forms among the fossil species, but this has been assumed by analogy with a number of recent species that are adapted to a benthonic mode of life. Recent Coleoidea often occur in large groups and because of the sometimes massive accumulations of rostra, especially of belemnites, it is assumed that the fossil species also lived in such communities. It should be borne in mind, however, that these accumulations could equally well be the result of transport, thus representing allochthonous thanatocoenosis. The fact that a particular nektonic species is found living in groups does not necessarily imply that their fossil remains will also occur together in a locality unless there has been some cause for their death en masse.

Arthropoda   More than three-quarters of all recent animal species belong to this phylum. By far the greater part are insects and will not be discussed here as they have a very limited geological signifi-cance. Of the many remaining groups, two will be considered: the ostracods and the trilobites which are both interesting palaeoecolo-gically.

Recent ostracods are chiefly marine animals, although a number of species live in brackish or fresh water. In Cainozoic deposits, where comparison with corresponding or closely related recent species is possible, ostracods provide a valuable aid to environ-mental studies, particularly with regard to salinity. In older deposits a comparison of this kind is not feasible. From the overall pattern of sediment and fauna in Palaeozoic deposits in which ostracods occur, it may, however, be inferred that this group must already have had the same range of adaptation particularly with regard to salinity as it has today.

Among the marine ostracods there are both pelagic and benthonic species. The pelagic species generally possess a more lightly built shell (carapace) than the benthonic; the latter forms have more ornamentation on the shell which is sometimes equipped with spines, particularly in species which live on muddy bottoms. Such spines may prevent the animal sinking into the sediment by increasing its surface area.

Most ostracods are omnivorous. Among the benthonic species there are many which feed on organic components in the sediment, and it is in such groups that species are found which can tolerate a certain amount of hydrogen sulphide in the environment. This explains the appearance of ostracods in some dark, fine-grained sediments in which pyrite is often present. Other species show a definite preference for sandy bottoms where the water movement ensures an adequate supply of oxygen.

Although most ostracods are found in shallow seas, there are a few groups, such as the Myocopoda, which live mainly in the bathyal zone.

All the available evidence indicates that the trilobites, unlike the ostracods, are exclusively marine. In many Palaeozoic seas the trilobites formed an important element of the fauna, and there are many ecological observations contained in the numerous publications which deal with this group. The conclusions reached by the various researchers often appear on comparison to be contradictory. In the present state of knowledge few generalisations can be made concerning the mode of life of the trilobites, particularly as a comparison with recent crustaceans is not always valid as Dollo has demonstrated. It is generally assumed that trilobites, like recent crustaceans, regularly shed their exoskeletons. The fragments of discarded exoskeleton would easily be transported and could therefore come to rest outside the actual environment of the species in question. Many accumulations of trilobite heads, or tailpieces, often of a single species, can be explained in this way. Although the influence of transportation is perhaps sometimes over-estimated, it is a factor that hampers the ecological investigation of the trilobites.

Very few trilobites are found in deposits whose lithological and palaeontological character indicates that they were formed in the vicinity of a coast. On the other hand, some trilobites form a characteristic element of a number of Palaeozoic reefs. It may be inferred that these trilobites actually lived on the reefs as the sediments between the individual reefs generally contain other species.

It appears from many studies that there is often a close connection between the lithological character of the sediment and the trilobites which are found there. This may indicate that such trilobites were benthonic and that their distribution was primarily dependent on the type of sediment. Trilobites in shales have more lightly built shells than those in limestones.

A large and varied group like the trilobites has almost certainly possessed the ability to adapt in various directions and it would be too sweeping a generalisation to regard all trilobites as benthonic. Clear criteria for distinguishing between benthonic species that creep or walk and nektonic species that swim are at present lacking. In either case the animals would propel themselves by means of their endopodites. In later crustaceans there is a definite relation between the development of the extremities and the method of propulsion but the trilobites afford no definitive answers on this point. The trilobite's divided appendage could function either for swimming or walking. The placing of the eyes provides no clue; some trilobites have laterally, others marginally placed eyes, but it is doubtful whether this is directly connected with a benthonic or a nektonic mode of life. Among the recent isopods there are excellent swimmers with lateral and even dorsal eyes, while some benthonic species possess marginally placed eyes. By analogy with observations from many other groups, flattening and lateral extension of the body is regarded as an adaptation to a benthonic mode of life.

Little is known for certain about the depth at which trilobites lived. The absence of sight organs figures largely in this discussion, but here too comparisons with recent crustaceans should be treated with some caution. Hypertrophy of the eyes, usually associated in trilobites with life in deep water, occurs in some recent crustaceans with a pelagic mode of life just below the surface. On the other hand Richter has shown that an appreciable reduction of the dimensions of the whole animal, as in some Upper Devonian species such as the Proetidae, may be associated with a bathypelagic mode of life, and may be the result of the less favourable conditions in which these reduced forms lived compared with the larger members of the same species in shallow seas.

Echinodermata Living echinoderms are all marine and mostly benthonic. Both their geographical distribution and their bathymetric range is very wide: they occur in all seas from high northern to high southern latitudes and from very shallow seas to the abyssal depths of the oceans. In existing seas echinoderms play an important role as bottom scavengers, many groups also being gregarious.

The mode of occurrence of fossil echinoderms suggests that they all inhabited marine environments. The fossil record shows moreover that Palaeozoic echinoderms were more diversified and more abundant, particularly in shallow seas, than afterwards. Living echinoderms can easily be grouped into four classes, but many more can easily be distinguished among Palaeozoic representatives of this phylum.

The hard components of an echinoderm, being formed in the mesoderm, constitute a true skeleton, although in its typical form it is a hollow test, external with regard to most of the organic structures. The skeleton is usually composed of many parts which can be loosely or firmly bound together. The parts may easily be loosened, and consequently complete skeletons of some groups are only preserved under unusual conditions.

The benthonic mode of life makes the echinoderms interesting from a palaeoecological point of view. But, notwithstanding the very large number of papers dealing with the systematic palaeontology of this phylum, relatively little work has been done so far with regard to their palaeoecology. The long record of the echinoderms and the rather marked differences between Palaeozoic and post-Palaeozoic echinoderms make it difficult to rely too much on the mode of life of living or Cainozoic echinoderms when drawing conclusions as to their Palaeozoic ancestors. With the predominant benthonic mode of life different adaptations occur; some are free-living, others are attached forms. Among the latter some may be free-living in maturity. In this as well as in other respects some groups may have changed their mode of life in the course of geological history.

Only two classes will be considered in somewhat more detail: the crinoids as a group of mainly attached echinoderms, and the echinoids as a group of free-living echinoderms.

Living crinoids are widely distributed in present-day seas. Although over 600 recent species are known, against something like 5000 fossil species, it is often assumed that living crinoids are only a mere vestige of a class that was more important long ago. It should be borne in mind, however, that among living representatives only a small minority retain the typical stalked pelmatozoan form of the sea lilies. The majority belong to comatulids, or feather stars, which in early life break from the stem and thereafter are free-living. Some families are confined to the littoral and sub-littoral zones, others such as the Antedonidae, the largest family of living crinoids, occur from the tidal zone to a depth of 6000 metres.

Remains of crinoids are abundant in many Palaeozoic and in some Mesozoic rocks. Sometimes the rock is largely made up of disarticulated columnals. In some cases these occur together with brachiopods, bryozoans or other groups, but in other cases enormous quantities of crinoids are the only organic material present. Close examination of such crinoid debris often shows little or no material from the main cup. A few cases are on record where teeth of shell feeding sharks are common in crinoidal limestones, and this may support the inference that sharks were potential enemies of the crinoids.

The high proportion of crinoid remains in some rocks of shallow-water origin suggests that dense populations of the animals existed in the past. The term " crinoid gardens " has sometimes been employed to denote this particular type of occurrence. Often abundant remains of crinoids are present together with inhabitants of reef environments, and although crinoids were probably not reef builders properly, they may have flourished on the flanks of many Palaeozoic bioherms. However, few detailed investigations have been carried out as to the palaeoecology of crinoids. This is the more regrettable as many evolutionary trends that have been revealed by careful systematic studies may be related to changes in their mode of life. A closer view of crinoid palaeoecology seems most promising.

Although the earliest known echinoids are known from Ordovician rocks, Palaeozoic representatives are extremely rare. It is only after the beginning of the Mesozoic that echinoids are among the more common fossils. Consequently a comparison between living and fossil species may be useful from a palaeoecological point of view, as is well evidenced by Nichols' (1959) study of the Cretaceous *Micraster*.

There is a rather marked difference between living regular and irregular echinoids as to their mode of life. Representatives of the first group generally inhabit rocky or other types of hard bottom, *e.g.*, coral reefs. Some live in natural depressions, others are rock-boring. The irregular echinoids, mainly spatangoids and clypeasteroids, live buried in sandy bottoms. Many peculiarities of their structure are related with this habit. There are, however, differences in the mode and the depth of burrowing, and in the way respiratory and feeding functions are maintained. Owing to the close relationship between such aspects in their mode of life and the features shown by the test, it seems likely that a detailed study of the test of echinoids may reveal many peculiarities of their life habits.

7. *The relationship between morphology and environment*

In his palaeoecological analysis the palaeontologist has to make use of the characters exhibited by the durable shells and skeletons of fossil organisms. He has to attempt to give an ecological interpretation of these characters. In Cainozoic deposits it is generally possible to make direct use of the results of ecological research, transferring the connection which has been established between organisms and environment for recent species to related fossil species. This is in general an acceptable method, although caution is always advisable. In older deposits, involving fossils which either do not have relations among recent fauna or do not allow the application of ecologically discovered connections, the characters of the individually encountered fossils must first be understood. This raises the difficult problem of the relation between the structure of the hard parts and the environment.

Most of the marine organisms with which the palaeontologist is concerned are benthonic animals. This is because the possession of a shell is less of an encumbrance for benthonic animals than it is for pelagic forms. An analogous example is the thin, hollow bones in the extremities of birds, as compared with the corresponding massive elements in land mammals.

This does not imply that pelagic animals cannot possess a shell: there are ample recent examples, such as foraminifers and radiolarians, to prove the contrary. It is going too far perhaps to suggest that the possession of a shell was associated with the origin of a benthonic mode of life, as Brooks suggested in explanation of the absence of Precambrian fossils.

It can be seen in many groups that there is a tendency in free-moving benthonic animals towards a flattening and broadening of the external form. In some fishes, such as the plaice, this even produces a rotation of the normal position of the body, whereby the plane of symmetry becomes horizontal. This in turn causes a shift in the position of some organs—noticeably the eyes. Many invertebrates show an adaptation to a benthonic mode of life, without such drastic changes as the flat fish have undergone. These phenomena have caused most researchers to associate a much flattened and broadened shape with a benthonic mode of life. A high measure of such adaptation is achieved by some genera of recent cuttlefish (e.g. *Sepia*). In trilobites (e.g. *Ogygia, Harpes*), in echinoids (e.g. *Clypeaster*) and in lamellibranchs (*Pecten*) equivalent forms occur which are almost certainly associated with a benthonic mode of life. The flat form with a large surface area can be considered both as an adaptation that prevents the animal sinking into a soft substratum, and as a development which reduces as far as possible the influence of the medium in movement over the substratum. The nature of the substratum may sometimes help to decide which is the more probable. In a few cases the form of the shell indicates that the weight has been distributed over as great a surface area as possible. This is the case in some lamellibranchs where the ribs or the hinge line are extended outside the periphery of the valve. Similar phenomena appear in some brachiopods (e.g. *Atrypa hystrix* and *Verneila cheiropteryx*).

A quite different sort of character associated with a benthonic mode of life is the occurrence of different colours on the upper and lower surfaces of an organism, as in flat fish, or of a striped pattern on the upper surface. This characteristic is rarely preserved in a fossil.

In sessile benthonic forms distinction can be made between (*i*) animals that burrow in the sea bed; (*ii*) animals that are attached to the substratum by their shells and (*iii*) animals with stalks that raise themselves above the substratum. The characters of burrowing organisms have already been referred to. With organisms that live on the bottom, whether directly attached to it or not, special mention must be made of the asymmetry which often develops in lamellibranchs under these circumstances (*Ostrea, Gryphaea*). This asymmetry can be so pronounced that the external lamellibranch features disappear entirely. This is the case with the rudists which display an outward resemblance to sessile, solitary corals. A similar development is known in brachiopods.

Many sessile benthonic animals occur in such numbers that they produce reefs. This is not only the case with corals, but also on a smaller scale in many other groups including the sponges, rudists and bryozoans.

The degree to which stalked forms raise themselves above the substratum varies greatly; in brachiopods it is minimal or non-existent; *Lingula* was probably a burrowing form; other brachiopods exhibit a tendency to enlarge their base by extending ribs or the hinge line, indicating that their brachial valves rested on the bottom. In crinoids the stem can be so long that the typical features of a sessile animal are more or less eliminated; a cup-shaped skeleton with arms emerges as the most characteristic form: it should be remembered that as a secondary characteristic the stem may disappear, possibly causing either the development of directly attached forms or of vagrant benthonic or pelagic forms.

A streamlined torpedo shape must be regarded as the ideal for the active swimmers among the pelagic animals. It is realised in many fishes, in some of the marine reptiles (e.g. *Ichthyosaurus*) and in some of the marine mammals (whales). This shape is sometimes approached quite closely in the invertebrates, as in the belemnites. Other adaptations are possible, however. In this connection mention should be made of the ammonites, many genera of which possess a well-streamlined form. Literature on the mode of life of the ammonites is, however, extensive and contradictory.

The problem of keeping the specific gravity within certain limits exists in all the pelagic animals. In active swimmers the effect of gravity, resulting from a specific gravity greater than that of the medium, can be compensated for by movement, while certain organs, such as the air-bladders of fishes, fulfil a hydrostatic function. Planktonic organisms do not have this compensation derived from active propulsion, and among these animals the percentage with shells or skeletons is much smaller than that in nektonic or benthonic forms. They often have ingenious organs that help to maintain their stability in the water. Graptolites for example, which were not all benthonic, were partly attached to other planktonic organisms, like seaweed, partly dependent on the organ with

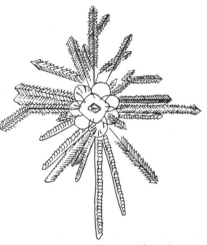

Fig. 26. Completely developed synrhabdosome of *Orthograptus*. After Bulman.

which each colony was equipped for this purpose (Fig. 26). Apart from the mode of life in the strict sense, other external factors of ecological importance exercise an influence on hard parts. It is well known that the secretion of lime is often more abundant in warm seas than in cooler waters, increasing the thickness of calcareous shells. Strong water movements, particularly in coastal areas, may produce an extra reinforcement of the shell, in the form of increased thickness, the development of ridges, etc. Conversely a reduction in salinity often leads to smaller and thinner shells. It is not certain how far this phenomenon is connected with a decrease in the lime content coupled with the salinity, with a diminution of mechanical requirements or with a general decline in the level of metabolism. It would not be correct, in any case, to associate all dwarf forms with a brackish environment.

8. *Palaeoecological conclusions*

In spite of a few pioneer studies at the beginning of this century, among which a special place is occupied by the fine analysis of the fauna of the Solnhofen limestone by Walther, palaeoecology is a very young branch of palaeontology. It is still at a stage that is comparable to that of the free-swimming larva of a benthonic animal; it can still move in any direction, perhaps under its own propulsion, perhaps driven by the current, but is not yet able to establish itself. The present state of palaeoecology is characterised by the almost complete lack of general laws. This is underlined by a number of summarising publications of recent years. Thus the very extensive second part of the *Treatise on marine ecology and paleoecology* (Ladd, 1957), devoted entirely to palaeoecology, consists almost wholly of a large number of separate palaeoecological analyses and bibliographical surveys. R. C. Moore (1957) in his otherwise very readable summary carefully avoids entering into the actual approach to palaeoecological problems. This also applies to the relevant chapter, *Allgemeine Grundlagen* (General principles), of the *Lehrbuch der Paläozoologie* by A. H. Müller (1957). Ager's *Principles of palaeoecology* (1963) is a most welcome addition to the general palaeoecological literature.

It even appears that there is no general consensus of opinion on the content of the term palaeoecology. Some writers use the term to embrace all research that has as its aim the acquisition of knowledge of the sedimentary environment, while others restrict the term to those investigations that make use of the fossil fauna and/ or flora, and are only concerned with the reconstruction of the biotope. There is no doubt that the latter application of the term is preferable. The reconstruction of the environment from the inorganic components of the sediment (the lithotope) belongs to general stratigraphy and not to palaeoecology which is part of palaeontology. The meaning of the word ecology permits no other interpretation of the term palaeoecology.

Although the number of palaeoecological publications has increased greatly in recent years, partly because of the growing realisation that palaeoecological analysis forms an essential link in the search for economically useful deposits, including coal, oil and ore-bearing formations (Ellison, 1955), much more fundamental research is necessary before it will be possible to formulate general laws.

The attempt must now be made to sketch the procedure for a palaeoecological analysis. It is generally known before the beginning of the investigation whether the object relates to continental or marine sediments. In the field the researcher's first task is to collect as much material as possible and to obtain as much quantitative data as possible concerning the orientation and position of the fossils in the sediment, and their vertical and horizontal distribution in the section. This means that the first stage of the investigation should go hand in hand with an accurate survey of the section, while as far as conditions permit, attention should also be given to the changes that occur in the direction of the stratification. Although investigation of the sediment itself does not strictly come within the palaeoecologist's scope, it is advisable to take orientated samples of the sediment, as those which contain fossils nearly always provide valuable additional data.

The next step is the systematic study of the fauna or flora which will give a picture of the quantitative distribution of all the elements encountered; the significance of the quantitative factor can hardly be over-estimated. In pollen analysis (a palaeontological method with a strong ecological slant) the value of this has long been realised. If the material is extensive enough, it is of importance to discover what the range of sizes is from each layer and from each species: are individuals of different dimensions mixed together or is there only one size present?

The fauna is classified as autochthonous or allochthonous, or a mixture, on the basis of the information thus obtained or collected in the field and compiled. If both autochthonous and allochthonous elements are present, the researcher must try to divide the fauna into its respective elements. Only then is it possible to achieve a reconstruction of the conditions in the biotope. The autochthonous, and thus benthonic elements, provide the primary data for this. On the basis of a comparison with recent related forms, or if these are lacking on what is generally known from ecology about the group in question, supplemented by special information from the examined material, the character of the biotope may be more or less sharply defined. In general it is true that the more varied the benthonic fauna, the sharper this definition becomes. If an autochthonous benthonic fauna is entirely lacking, the possibility that the bottom conditions in the locality were unsuitable for a normal fauna must be considered. The answer can usually be found in the character of the sediment.

The allochthonous elements, although ecologically alien, can also be a considerable help in reconstructing the conditions of the biotope. The very fact that these allochthonous elements could be transported and become part of the sediment throws light on one aspect of the environment. A closer study of the allochthonous components, carried out on the same lines as for the autochthonous part, shows with which other biotope or biotopes there was a connection. The larger the relative size of the allochthonous part, the smaller the distance or the easier the connection must have been. The allochthonous part of the fauna, particularly when it is ecologically well defined, can provide valuable supplementary information for the reconstruction of the biotope. Continental elements in an autochthonous marine fauna are an example.

Finally reference should be made to another important point. A biotope is always limited in both time and space; horizontally one biotope gives place to another with different characters, while vertically, that is to say in time as represented by sediments that lie stratigraphically higher, it is succeeded by another biotope, again with different properties. The study of these sequences provides the palaeontologist with new data of a different category. If the geological conditions indicate no significant interruptions in the sedimentary sequence, then each biotope must gradually pass into the next and the pattern of ecological succession must therefore correspond with these gradual changes. As soon as a particular tendency in development can be recognised, it can be used to help fill in the phases of the pattern that are ecologically less clearly defined. The analysis of the fauna from the Upper Permian of Kansas by Elias (1937) may be quoted as an example. The complex investigated is characterised by a particular rhythmic sedimentation, which runs parallel with rhythmical changes in the fauna. Elias showed that both could be reduced to a rhythmical change in the depth of the water. Through the recognition of this tendency it was possible to indicate the conditions in which the successive fauna lived more precisely than would otherwise have been possible for each of the individual phases.

Something comparable applies to the sequence of different biotopes in a particular chrono-stratigraphic unit. These must have been able to exist alongside each other and are thus able to provide reciprocal support for the interpretation of the different parts. The bathymetric zones that Scott (1940) was able to identify on the basis of ammonites in the Cretaceous of Texas illustrate this. Here, too, the recognition of a trend made possible an interpretation of the parts that would have been less likely and less convincing on the basis of the parts considered separately.

In certain circumstances the vertical sequence can be a repetition of the horizontal, which provides a new argument in the interpretation of the sequence in time.

It is obvious from the above that regional palaeoecological research leads to a real deepening of palaeontological understanding. However desirable studies in detail may be, there is no doubt that a fundamental increase of palaeoecological knowledge must come from large scale regional studies, such as those now being conducted by the American Petroleum Institute in the Gulf Coast area.

CHAPTER 3

THE HORIZONTAL DISTRIBUTION OF
FOSSILS: GEOGRAPHICAL FACTORS

1. *Introduction*

The previous chapter showed how the distribution of fossil and recent organisms is influenced by environmental factors. In the case of fossils, the effect of transport after death also has to be taken into account. There is also a complex of quite different factors involved in the distribution of organisms over the Earth. If the fauna of the North Sea is compared with that of the mudflats of the Waddenzee, it is clear that the great differences between these two adjacent and inter-connected areas are the result of ecological factors, such as salinity, depth of water, tides and bottom conditions. If the fauna of the North Sea is compared with that of an ecologically similar area on the east coast of North America, it will be apparent that the faunas of the two regions have only a very few elements in common. The very slight ecological differences which naturally exist between the two areas can hardly be responsible for their obvious faunal differences. The factors involved in this case are of a geographical nature.

It can be shown by some unintentionally conducted experiments that ecological factors are not determinative in such cases. For example the lamellibranch *Petricola pholadiformis*, a species of North American origin, has spread gradually along the coasts of Western Europe since about 1890 and is now ousting *Barnea candida* which occupies roughly the same ecological niche. The American species, having once been brought here, is thriving. A few other examples will be discussed later in this chapter.

Both ecological and geographical factors determine the distribution of plants and animals. These two groups of factors cannot always be sharply differentiated, and it even could be argued that geographical factors are ultimately reducible to ecological ones, since what has been called the result of geographical conditions above can also be regarded as the consequence of the ecological conditions of the intervening area. The difference between the shelf faunas on either side of the Atlantic could then be regarded as resulting from the presence of the oceanic biotope which separates two shelf biotopes. The present distribution of organisms can therefore be approached from either an ecological or a geographical angle. For plants the work of Dansereu (1957) is ecologically orientated, that of Good (1947) geographically. In zoogeography there is a similar distinction between the work of Hesse, Allee and Schmidt (1951) on the one hand, and of de Beaufort (1951) and Ekman (1953) on the other.

Geologically, however, there is much to be said for making a clear distinction between ecological and geographical factors. Not only is some of the data which is available to the geologist of a different character from that of the investigator of present-day floras and faunas but also the problem is differently stated. Between biogeography and palaeobiogeography there exists the same kind of difference of emphasis as between ecology and palaeoecology. Whereas the biogeographer can observe the present geographical pattern of the world directly, the palaeobiogeographer must attempt to draw palaeogeographical conclusions from his observation of the distribution pattern of the organisms. It would, however, be incorrect to infer from this that the relationship between biogeography and palaeobiogeography is entirely comparable with that existing between ecology and palaeoecology. It was already obvious in the time of the classic descriptive biogeography that the present distribution of plants and animals on the Earth is only comprehensible as the result of a long history of evolution.

This historic evolution embraces not only changes in geographical pattern, but also changes in the organism itself. Floral and faunal differences between different areas therefore appear to result not only from ecological and geographical causes, but also from divergent tendencies within the organic world which are clearly a function of time. The longer two regions have been separated, the greater the evolutionary divergence their floras and faunas will display. The problem of the distribution of organisms can therefore be approached from the evolutionary angle as well as from the ecological and the geographical ones. Simpson made the evolutionary approach in a particularly readable essay (1953).

Therefore this chapter is devoted to the distribution of fossils, as affected by geographical factors. The geographical pattern of distribution of plants and animals can only be understood in terms of a historical (geological) evolution. This applies not only to the distribution of fossil floras and faunas at any moment in the past, but equally to the distribution of recent floras and faunas which is no more than the record of a moment in a long geological development. This implies that the biogeography of recent organisms is a science which shows close affinities to historical geology, as soon as it leaves the purely descriptive stage, and this is a reason for referring occasionally in the course of this discussion to the much better known distribution of recent organisms.

Palaeobiogeography, the history of the distribution of fossil organisms, is a little practised but exciting branch of historical palaeontology. It can furnish valuable data for other fields of biological and geological research. Acquaintance with the centres of evolution and the migration routes of different groups of organisms is essential for an understanding of their evolution. Palaeobiogeography is useful in stratigraphic palaeontology, often showing how the appearance of a particular group of fossils in a particular area may be long delayed by geographical factors, and thus fail to provide a usable criterion for chronological correlations. Finally palaeobiogeography forms one of the bases of palaeogeography. The constantly changing geographical pattern of the Earth leaves no direct traces—each successive image erases the former. It is the sediments, and particularly the fossils preserved within them, that enable the sequences of past geography to be reconstructed.

2. *Migration*

Before going more deeply into palaeobiogeography it is necessary to consider the way in which organisms are distributed and the external factors, favourable or adverse, which influence this.

The distribution of animals is to a great extent dependent on their means of movement which may be active or passive. There are great differences between the groups in this respect. Many birds are able to cover large distances in a short time, crossing extensive tracts of ocean, desert or mountain which would not offer them suitable habitats. The distribution of many good fliers among the birds is principally determined by environmental factors. The geographical accessibility of the area is of little importance. The influence of the geographical factor increases as the flight capacity decreases. The ease with which birds can spread over the earth contrasts sharply with the limited capacities of sessile benthonic organisms, and between these two extremes lies a whole range of possibilities. Many insects are known to be able to fly over unsuitable environments to reach and populate favourable habitats, and in this respect they are the equals of some of the birds. Land mammals are by their nature earthbound, but most of them are nevertheless capable of crossing quite large stretches of water in safety. Under the pressure of increasing population density, animals may spread from a region where conditions are ideal to areas that are less favourable ecologically; these can serve as transit zones as long as they offer minimal means of subsistence to a limited number of individuals.

The many marine benthonic invertebrates which undergo a pelagic larval stage form a separate category. Although this stage is usually of short duration, varying in different groups from a few minutes to a few months, it is of great significance from the biogeographical point of view, because the strong ecological connection of the adult animals is temporarily severed. For many sessile benthonic animals this is the only chance of extending their area of distribution. For animals that are not sessile this stage often provides an opportunity for by-passing ecologically unsuitable zones. During this short period a pelagic mode of life neutralises the limiting factors of depth of water or bottom conditions. Actively swimming, or borne by the current, the larvae can subsequently develop in a new area, providing they reach it at the appropriate moment. The speed of migration depends on the duration of the free, larval stage, on the speed of travel of the organism and on the time needed for the animal to reach sexual maturity. A simple calculation will show that distances of thousands of kilometres can in practice be covered in comparatively short periods of geological time. The manner in which the distribution of plants is effected is

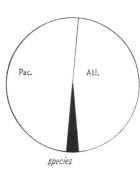
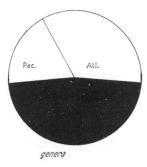

BRACHYURA (CRUST.)

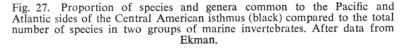

ECHINODERMATA

Fig. 27. Proportion of species and genera common to the Pacific and Atlantic sides of the Central American isthmus (black) compared to the total number of species in two groups of marine invertebrates. After data from Ekman.

to some extent comparable, the dispersal of seeds or spores corresponding to the larval stage.

A more detailed discussion of what might be termed the biological factors of animal and plant distribution lies beyond the scope of this book. Enough has been said to make it clear that an understanding of the history of distribution of a particular species or group is not possible without studying the potentialities of the organisms concerned.

The distribution of organisms is naturally influenced by external circumstances as well as by factors inherent in the creatures themselves. The spread of particular organisms at a particular place may be favoured, tolerated, hampered or prevented by these external conditions which are directly connected with the geographical pattern of the Earth. Thus the Central American isthmus, for example, forms an insurmountable barrier to the interchange of marine elements between the tropical belt of the eastern Pacific and the Caribbean. There is no possibility of migration around North of South America for stenothermic species, as these typical warm water inhabitants find their way blocked by a temperature barrier. Nevertheless the stenothermic faunas on either side of the isthmus display a considerable degree of relationship, not so much in the species as in the genera (Fig. 27). This phenomenon is further accentuated because many of these genera are by no means global in their distribution, being limited to the two areas quoted. This apparently strange distribution pattern becomes comprehensible if the historical factor is taken into account: direct migration between the two areas used to be possible. It is apparent from the geological history of the region that the present geographical pattern did not come into being until the Pliocene. Prior to this, there was a long period, with some interruptions during which the interchange of marine elements between the tropical east Pacific and the Caribbean Sea was possible. The moment at which the barrier came into being for the last time explains the fact that there is a greater correspondence at the level of the genera than at that of the species. Most genera are pre-Pliocene and were thus able to make use of the connection existing at an earlier stage in their evolution. The species are mostly post-Pliocene, and are the result of further evolution within the genera after they had been separated by the Central American isthmus. After this separation evolution followed distinct courses in the two regions

As this process advanced, the relationship decreased. Two regions that have become separated in this manner will ultimately have no genera in common. The existence of an earlier connection may still be apparent from correspondence in the higher taxonomic categories. In general the taxonomic level at which the relationship is still expressed is an indication of the age of the dividing barrier.

At the same moment as the Central American isthmus began to

function as a barrier for marine elements, there emerged a route which made possible the interchange of land elements between North and South America. In Section 5 it will be seen that the increased affinity in the mammalian faunas of North and South America since the Pliocene reflects this change in geographical pattern. The influence of this change, however, is not particularly obvious; the great length and extreme narrowness of this isthmus makes it a possible but by no means ideal migration route, and it has been traversed by a comparatively small number of species and individuals. For mammals a passage such as that between Europe and Asia is much more favourable. A chain of islands is even less favourable to migration than an isthmus, but in the course of time a number of purely land animals will succeed in spreading themselves by means of a defective link of this type. The time factor is involved here, making successful migration something of a gamble.

For land-based birds and flying insects an island chain forms a more practical passage, although an element of chance is always present. An illustration of this is afforded by a comparison of the insect faunas of Australia with those of the islands of the south west Pacific which become less related as the distance increases.

A similar disparity in the quality of different migratory routes exists for marine animals. The shelf fauna along the west coast of Central America is limited on the east by the isthmus; and to the west the ocean forms a hardly less effective barrier. As the ocean is undoubtedly older than the isthmus, the apparently remarkable phenomenon arises of the shelf fauna of the eastern Pacific showing a much greater affinity with that of the Caribbean than with its counterpart in the Indo-Pacific area.

An ocean basin that forms a largely impenetrable barrier for a shelf fauna provides an ideal migratory route for a typical pelagic fauna. Analogous differences for groups with different ecological requirements can be observed in other geographical patterns. An island chain forms a quite serious obstacle to the distribution of truly oceanic elements, such as most whales; at the very least it has a pronounced filter effect. For typical littoral elements, however, an island chain offers better prospects than the open sea.

In the following paragraphs a number of similar examples will be discussed. The cases quoted above are sufficient to demonstrate that in nature there is no simple division into barriers which prevent and routes which allow migration. For a correct assessment of biogeographical problems it is often necessary to take a number of factors into account: the ecology of the group of organisms in question; their potentiality for active or passive migration, possibly during a larval stage; the quality of the land or sea link; and the evolution of the relevant geographical pattern.

3. *Shallow marine faunas*

From the geological point of view the shallow marine fauna is of particular significance as a great percentage of all marine fossils belongs to this category.

This fauna, regarded for the present purpose as an entity, is chiefly distributed in a belt of varying width along the margins of the continents, bounded on one side by the coastline and on the other by the continental slope. Both of these boundaries can naturally be regarded as ecological limits, but taken on a world scale they can equally well be considered as geographical. As the shelves enclose each continent and come into contact in a few places such as the Bering Strait and the Malay Archipelago, the potential distribution of shelf fauna would be very considerable if it were not conditioned by climatological factors. The effect of these is particularly noticeable in the present geographical pattern of the world. Whereas the climatic zones roughly follow lines of latitude, the natural boundaries of the continental shelves run largely according to the meridian circles. Shelf faunas along the various continental coasts show an obvious climatic zoning with the result that the interchange of shelf elements between comparable shelf areas of different continents, or two sides of one continent, is relatively rare.

Although there is good reason for supposing that climatological factors also conditioned the distribution patterns of earlier shelf faunas, it appears from palaeontological evidence that their distributions were often more uniform in the past.

This is evident in the shelf faunas of warm waters. The recent shelf faunas of the tropical and subtropical zones illustrate by their relationship in genera and families, more than in species, that interchange must have been much more common in the past.

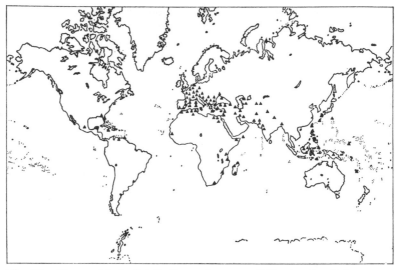

Fig. 28.   Geographical distribution of nummulitids in the Palaeogene.
After Joleaud.

Palaeontologists have long known that there exists a close relationship among the shelf faunas in a belt from the Indo-West Pacific
area via the Mediterranean to Central America. Various groups of
fossils, including such extinct groups as the rudists and the num-
mulites (Fig. 28) are entirely or largely restricted to this belt. The
influence can be traced of a totally different geographical pattern,
where the migration of shelf species was possible within a roughly
east-west belt. There can be no doubt that this was due to the
Tethys.

The distribution of reef-building corals, a typical group of
benthonic animals from warm seas, is very illuminating in this
respect. According to Gerth (1925) of the 35 genera known from
the Palaeogene of the Malay Archipelago, 12 are distributed
throughout the whole of the Tethys region including the West
Indies. Many of the coral species are distributed through the
whole of the Old World Tethys region, but at the lowest taxonomic
level the degree of relationship between the Tethys in the Old
World and in Central America is much smaller. This shows that
since the beginning of the Palaeogene, migration between Eurasia
and Central America has been less easy. The relationship of the

Eurasian coral faunas among themselves appears to be closer than that between any one of them and the coral fauna of Central America, demonstrating that the latter area became separated from the Old World Tethys region by a barrier that was difficult to penetrate.

The picture presented by the reef-building corals is repeated in general outline in many other groups, although the pattern is not always so clearly defined. This is because the opportunity for distribution in benthonic reef-building corals is restricted to the larval period. In recent related forms this lasts for at most a few weeks and sometimes no more than a few days.

The problem now arises as to whether Central America was connected with the Tethys region of the Old World via the Atlantic or the Pacific. To find an answer it is necessary first to examine more closely the Atlantic and Pacific sectors of the Central American region. Although these are unmistakably related, the western Atlantic area shows a much more obvious connection with the Tethys fauna of the Old World than the eastern Pacific area. The relationship between the eastern Pacific and the Indo-West Pacific area is in turn less close than that between the western Atlantic and the Mediterranean area. Species that are common to both the West Indian and the Malay areas are practically always, and in some groups exclusively, those that are also found in the Mediterranean area. It follows from this that Central America must be regarded as a westward extension of the Tethys with which it was connected via the Atlantic Ocean. The Atlantic formed a much less serious obstacle to the spread of many elements of the Tethys fauna than the Pacific.

The evident relationship that existed in the Palaeogene between the various parts of the Tethys came to an end in the Neogene. The folding, followed by elevation, which took place in the Tethys geosyncline of the Old World caused the fragmentation of the formerly continuous sea. Migration between the various areas ceased, and this produced divergent evolution with a consequent decrease in the degree of relationship between the faunas of the now isolated parts. This development is coupled with a marked impoverishment, especially in the Mediterranean area: reef-building corals are scarce in the Neogene of this region while they show a richly varied evolution in the Malay area. The main centre of their distribution has obviously shifted. Many Palaeogene corals from the Mediterranean area that died out in or before the Neogene are encountered in the Neogene of the Indo-West Pacific area. It is important to note that none of these species is found in the Neogene of the Caribbean area. Generally similar phenomena can also be seen in other groups. The mainstream of migration evidently passed from west to east (Fig. 29).

The historical evolution that produced the situation outlined above has not always been taken sufficiently into account, with the result that the Mediterranean Tethys fauna has sometimes been characterised as Indo-West Pacific—a supposition that is generally invalid. Mortensen has pointed out that the echinoderm fauna of the Mediterranean area is much richer than that of the Indo-West Pacific, a difference that is too great to be attributed exclusively to a disparate amount of research in the two regions. The same is probably true for the marine mammals. The Mediterranean area was undoubtedly an important distribution centre within the Tethys belt.

A number of interesting points in the evolution of the Tethys fauna require individual attention. When the so-called Paratethys

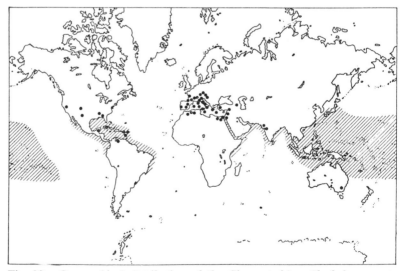

Fig. 29.   Geographical distribution of the Clypeasteridae. *Shaded*: present distribution; *black dots*: Cainozoic fossil localities (most dots represent a group of localities). After Joleaud, with additions.

was divided in the Neogene into three separate basins (the Pan-
nonian, Euxine, and the Uralo-Caspian), a fauna of a special
character developed. Reduction of salinity caused the disappearance
of stenohaline elements (corals, echinoderms, cephalopods), and
forms with a certain tolerance to brackish water, particularly
molluscs, became predominant. As a whole this fauna displays the
pattern that is characteristic of such special environments: little
variety of species and a great abundance of individuals.

The bryozoan reefs which developed locally in these basins form
a remarkable counterpart to those of the Upper Permian Zechstein
Sea, which similarly had a special environment.

Another point that attracts attention in the evolution of the
Tethys fauna is its gradual impoverishment, especially in the
eastern Atlantic region which includes the Mediterranean area.
This impoverishment becomes very obvious as soon as the influence
of the Alpine tectogenesis is perceptible in the geographical pattern,

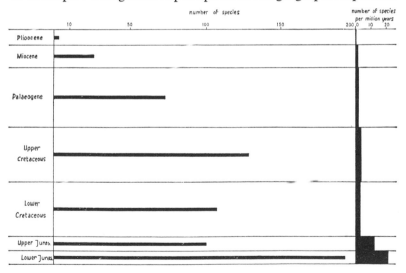

Fig. 30.   Decline of the Cidaroidea, a group of sea urchins, in the European
part of the Tethys from the Middle Jurassic to the Pliocene.

but in fact the phenomenon is much older. Fig. 30 illustrates this
for the Cidaroidea. Although the periods of time compared are
not of equal duration, the phenomenon is constant if this disparity
is compensated for. The recent shelf fauna of the Mediterranean

Sea has only two species of this group, the Indo-Malayan area 48. Fig. 30 demonstrates not only the gradual impoverishment of the fauna, but also its richness during the Mesozoic. The figures of many other groups show an analogous pattern.

The few facts given above, which could easily be supplemented with many others, clearly show the significance of the Tethys as a biogeographical element in the Palaeogene. Indirectly it may be deduced from the relationship which existed between the various parts of this belt in the Palaeogene that the influence of the Tethys on the distribution of shelf fauna previously must have been even greater.

Various researchers, notably Neumayr, Uhlig and Diener, had indicated long ago the great importance of the Tethys for the distribution of the Mesozoic fauna. Arkell (1956, ch. 27, 28), relying on better and more plentiful palaeontological and strati-graphical data, has recently worked out Jurassic biogeography, especially of the ammonites, in much greater detail (Figs. 31, 32). One of the most interesting conclusions to which Arkell's pains-taking palaeontological and stratigraphical analysis has led is that earlier investigators have almost always generalised too much. Even

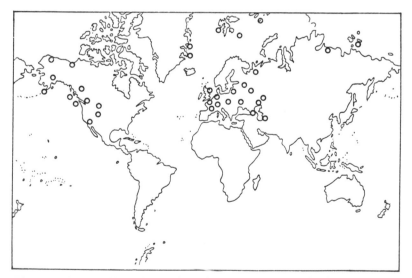

Fig. 31. Geographical distribution of the boreal ammonite family Cardio-ceratidae in the Callovian and the Lower Oxfordian. After Arkell.

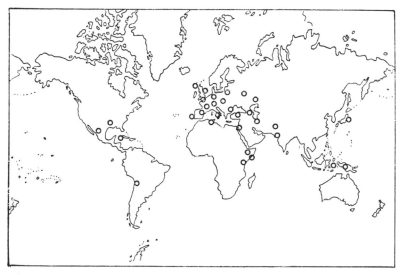

Fig. 32.   Geographical distribution of the *Perisphinctes* fauna in the Upper Oxfordian, exemplifying an ammonite group whose distribution is principally restricted to the Tethys area.

in a comparatively short period such as the Jurassic, the pattern changed too much and too often to be represented in a single, generalised picture. Certain points, however, are immediately obvious. As has already been seen in the Palaeogene, the Pacific also appears to have been the most important barrier during the Jurassic. The relationship existing between the eastern Pacific and the Indo-West Pacific areas seems to have come into being via the Old World. Only two or three genera show a typically Pacific distribution pattern. As these genera are not distributed round the circumference of the Pacific, Arkell assumes that they succeeded in crossing directly over the ocean, a route that would not have been impossible for animals like the ammonites. In addition there are a few genera which are distributed exclusively in the eastern Pacific, along the western coasts of the two Americas. These facts do not support the many earlier palaeographical reconstructions which represent the Pacific in the Jurassic as a mainly land area. Others, among them Stille (1948), have regarded the Pacific as an old ocean.

In contrast the distribution of the Jurassic ammonites around the Indian Ocean may indicate that this is a young ocean. It is difficult to reconcile the existence of an Indian Ocean in Jurassic times with the extremely small degree of relationship between the Jurassic ammonites of Madagascar and those of Indonesia. The Tethys and a southern arm of this palaeogeographic sea apparently formed the only possible connection.

Little is known of the pre-Mesozoic history of the Tethys. It see.ns probable from the distribution of the Permian ammonoids, however, that it was in existence in this period as a faunal migration route. Of the 58 ammonoid genera known from the Permian, nine are known to be common to the four celebrated Permian ammonoid localities: Texas, Sicily, the Urals and Timor. At first sight this may seem a comparatively small percentage but it should be remembered (*i*) that of the 58 genera, 17 are known from one area only (some of these are specialised forms from rather eccentrically situated areas) and (*ii*) that the four areas compared occupy only a limited part of the Permian stratigraphically. Of the five stages generally distinguished at present the Urals have only the lowest two in marine facies and Sicily only the middle one. If the fauna from the Alpine area (Carnic Alps, Croatia) is added to that of Sicily, the correspondence is greater, rising to more than 25 per cent, not including eccentric forms. It appears that the Atlantic formed a considerable barrier in the Permian as well as in the Mesozoic; that is indicated by the greater degree of inter-relationship within the Tethys of the Old World than between the Old World, and Texas and Mexico. The close relationship between the Permian ammonoid faunas of Timor and Texas is curious. Whether this should be ascribed to trans-Pacific migration, or whether it is merely a misleading conclusion arrived at in the absence, so far, in the western part of the Old World Tethys of adequate Permian sections with rich ammonoid faunas, must remain unresolved at present.

The Carboniferous fusulines should be mentioned as an example of other Palaeozoic animals whose distribution was evidently influenced by the Tethys. The relationship discovered by Shirley between the Devonian brachiopods of Western Europe and New Zealand may also be ascribed, perhaps, to migration along the Tethys coasts.

Few positive indications of the existence of the Tethys are to be

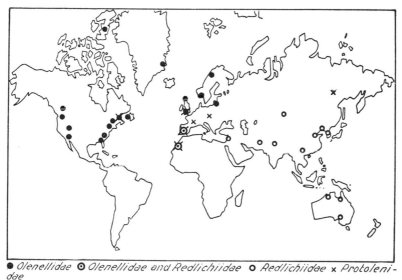

● *Olenellidae* ◉ *Olenellidae and Redlichiidae* ○ *Redlichiidae* × *Protoleni-dae*

Fig. 33. Geographical distribution of trilobites in the Lower Cambrian. After Hupé.

○ *Paradoxides* ◐ *Paradoxides and Centropleura* ● *Centropleura*
× *Kootenia Olenoides and Oryctocephalus*

Fig. 34. Geographical distribution of trilobites in the Middle Cambrian. After Hupé.

8

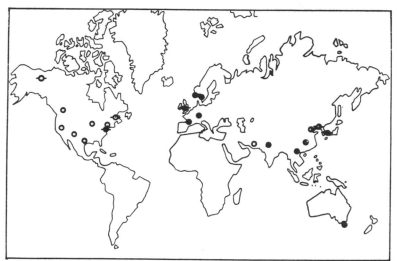

-O- *Hungaidae* and *Dikellocephalidae* ● *Hungaidae* O *Dikellocephalidae*

Fig. 35.   Geographical distribution of certain trilobite families in the Upper
Cambrian and the Ordovician. After Hupé.

found in the distribution of Lower Palaeozoic groups, of which the
Archaeociathidae and the graptolites are typical. However, the
Cambrian trilobites, one of the few Lower Palaeozoic groups whose
geographical distribution has been well studied (Hupé, Wilson),
indicate that the Tethys already formed a migration route between
Europe and Asia, although it may then have been less important
geographically than in later periods (Figs. 33-35).

In the Lower Cambrian,. two trilobite provinces have long been
distinguished: a western province characterised by Olenellidae
which embraces Western Europe and North America; and an
eastern one characterised by Redlichiidae which not only includes
eastern Asia and Australia but is continued via an early Palaeozoic Tethys to south-western Europe and North Africa. In Spain
and North Africa elements from both provinces appear together,
without causing a further interchange.

In the Middle Cambrian a separate North Atlantic province can
be distinguished, taking in Western Europe and the easternmost
parts of North America and characterised by *Paradoxides*. If it is
true that *Paradoxides* evolved from the Olenellidae, this North

Atlantic province could be regarded as a reduced vestige of the Lower Cambrian Olenellidae province. Western North America shows affinities with Asia. Pacific elements, however, are also found in eastern North America in a belt that runs close to the distribution area of the Atlantic elements. It is usually assumed that the two Middle Cambrian provinces were separated by a barrier, but it is questionable whether this assumption is correct. Wilson (1957) has pointed out in a recent study of Upper Cambrian trilobites that purely ecological factors have had a greater influence than was formerly assumed. The distribution of the Upper Cambrian Olenellidae appears to be linked with the black shales of the geosynclines. They are absent from the fringe areas of the kratons which have a different sedimentary type and their place is taken by a great variety of other trilobites. If Wilson's thesis is correct, there is no longer any justification for the undeniably arbitrary construction that is to be seen on all palaeogeographical maps of the Cambrian.

There can be little doubt that the Tethys faunas of the Palaeogene and the Mesozoic, such as the corals, echinoids and rudists, belonged to warm waters. Although these faunas had a wide distribution, even extending outside the actual Tethys area, this does not imply that there were not other faunas in these periods inhabiting different climatic areas. Faunas are known from both the Jurassic (Fig. 31) and the Cretaceous which may reasonably be assumed to have had a more Boreal character. The contrast between a different Mediterranean and a Boreal realm is reflected with particular clarity in the faunal character of the European Cretaceous. The regression, which set in at the end of the Jurassic and resulted in the transition from Jurassic to Cretaceous being developed in continental facies in a large part of Western Europe, caused a division in the marine Cretaceous. This division lasted until the Upper Cretaceous when it was partially effaced during the great transgression of this period. In the course of the Lower Cretaceous a transgression gradually extended from the Mediterranean region, via northern France, to southern England. This transgression spread elements of the Mediterranean fauna, such as rudists, echinoids and many ammonite genera, over much of Western Europe. At the same time a Boreal sea extended across the northern parts of Germany, Holland and England. This

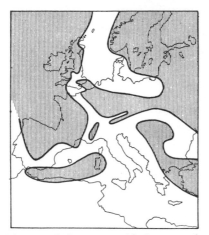

Fig. 36. Palaeogeographical map of Western Europe during the Aptian, with the first connection between the Mediterranean and the Boreal Cretaceous Sea. After Wills.

sea had a different faunal character, with belemnites as the most typical element. As long as there was no contact between these two seas, their faunal identity was preserved. A mingling of Mediterranean and Boreal elements first appears in northern England in the Aptian, indicating that the first contact between the two seas took place here (Fig. 36). It is apparent from the distribution of certain Mediterranean elements that connections between the northern and southern seas also came into being in Eastern Europe during the Cretaceous. These connections were probably all in the nature of comparatively narrow straits between the Palaeozoic massifs. Large-scale interchange of Mediterranean and Boreal elements did not occur until the Upper Cretaceous, when large parts of these massifs were themselves covered by the Cretaceous transgression, and the individual faunal characters of the two regions were largely lost. Only a few groups, such as the rudists, retained their former limited distribution which could indicate that climatological factors were still operative even after the geographical barriers to distribution had been removed.

The regression at the end of the Cretaceous created a long-lasting and more sharply defined division between the Mediterranean and Boreal marine provinces. A part of the region that had been on the northern edge of the Mediterranean sphere of influence in the Mesozoic came within the Boreal sphere after the end of the Cretaceous. This is particularly the case with the Paris Basin, that was again flooded by the sea from the north or the north-west in the Palaeogene. Although pronounced Mediterranean groups, including the nummulitids, still penetrated into the area, these occasioned no general change in the character of the fauna. From the faunal point of view, the Palaeogene Paris Basin is primarily a southward continuation of the North Sea. In the course of the Neogene the Boreal character of the North Sea fauna was further accentuated. The continuing regression caused a further contraction of the fauna of the North Sea area, and more and more Mediterranean species disappeared. Finally the climate of the Pleistocene caused still further migrations. Arctic forms penetrated not only to the North Sea, but even as far as the Mediterranean Sea.

The history of the Pleistocene forms a particularly interesting subject of zoogeographical study. The development of its faunal pattern was determined not only by the shift of climatic boundaries and the migrations this caused, but also by purely geographical factors. The geographical conditions of the North Sea formed no obstacle to the immigration of Boreal and Arctic species, but circumstances were quite different for Mediterranean species. In principle two routes were open to the latter: (*i*) around the north of Scotland and (*ii*) through the narrow passage at the southern end of the North Sea. The first route contains a " high climatological threshold " which was almost invariably fatal even for species potentially capable of surviving in the southern part of the North Sea. In the second route the funnel shape of the sea served at least to check migration; this route was moreover repeatedly closed. A remarkable phenomenon resulting from the form and situation of the North Sea is the fact that the interglacial transgressions in the first instance also caused an expansion of Boreal elements. The zoogeographical history of the North Sea has not yet been sufficiently studied: only its evolution since the last Ice Age which is of immediate importance for the understanding of the present fauna has received much attention. The same applies to the Baltic where postglacial history with its alternation of fresh and salt water phases forms a remarkable example of the interplay of ecological and geographical factors.

The points discussed above make it sufficiently clear that the history of the geographical distribution of marine faunas is not only a fascinating study in itself, forming an essential link in the historical evolution of the Earth, but one which influences many aspects of applied palaeontology. Knowledge of the history of the geographical distribution of marine faunas is necessary for making

stratigraphical correlations (Chapter 4) and for a proper understanding of the evolutionary history of different groups (Chapter
5). This naturally applies to continental faunas and floras as well,
but it is particularly in the study of marine faunas that palaeontologists' lack of biogeographical interest has been most keenly
felt. Marine faunas, after all, are the palaeontologist's primary
material. Neontologists have ventured into this territory, but for
obvious reasons their interest does not extend very far back in
time. It is primarily the task of the palaeontologist to tackle this
aspect of the subject and to give it its proper place as a branch
of palaeontology.

4. *Continental faunas*

Continental faunas and floras have contributed even more to the
reconstruction of the Earth's palaeogeography than marine faunas.
This is due both to the character of the faunas themselves and to the
nature of the continents. The elements of continental faunas are
attached more closely to their environments than those of marine
faunas. They do not experience anything comparable to the larval,
pelagic stage of many marine animals, in which the creature is
released for a short time from its normal environment. They are,
therefore, the obvious organisms from which information about
former interinsular and intercontinental connections can be
obtained.

The term continental is applied here to faunas in the same sense
as Twenhofel used it for facies, and therefore includes both animals
that live on dry land, and aquatic animals that live in land surface
waters such as lakes and rivers. Flying faunas (e.g. birds, insects)
can also be added since these are always attached in some degree
to the land. Biogeographically, however, they fall within a different
category.

A very reliable group, biogeographically, is formed by the true
freshwater fishes which cannot tolerate brackish or salt water. As
this criterion can hardly be verified in older faunas, it is only
usable in very recent ones. A good example is furnished by the
river fish of the Great Sunda islands and the neighbouring continent of South East Asia (Fig. 37). The great degree of correspondence between these two regions has long been known and is

explained by their geological history. In the Pleistocene the sea level fell sufficiently from time to time to leave the Sunda shelf dry. The river systems which have since been separated by the most recent rise in sea level would then have formed one whole, making an extensive interchange of species possible. These events have occurred so recently that the great degree of correspondence at species level is understandable. A further argument for the correctness of this explanation is provided by a comparison of the fish fauna in the rivers of west and east Borneo. The rivers of east Borneo, the Mahakam and others, flowed directly into the deep Macassar Strait and therefore had no connection with the rivers of the Sunda system even at times when the sea level was low. The east Borneo rivers have their own special faunal character with a high percentage of endemic species; and only a few of their species are also known from West Borneo or from Java and Sumatra (de Beaufort, 1926). A further comparison within the whole region not only supplies a satisfactory explanation of the present distribution pattern, but, conversely, illuminates the geographical nature of the area in the Pleistocene.

The land mammals are another group which lend themselves to this type of research. G. G. Simpson has devoted a great deal of time to them (for a summary see Simpson, 1953). On the basis of a careful analysis of the Cainozoic fauna he made a qualitative classification of the various intercontinental connections, distinguishing them as " corridors ", " filters ", and " sweepstakes routes ". An example of the first is found between Europe and Asia. In a connection of this type mutual interchange of elements takes place

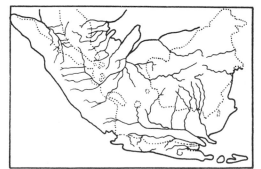

Fig. 37.   Palaeogeographical map of the Sunda region during the last ice age. The dotted lines show the present coastlines.

on a large scale, and the result is that the mammalian faunas of Western Europe and Eastern Asia display a much greater relationship than, for example, those of Western Europe and Central Africa, in spite of the smaller distance separating the latter pair.

A long, narrow connection, such as the present isthmus between North and South America, has in contrast a strong filter effect. Only a fraction of the fauna is able to make successful use of it. The

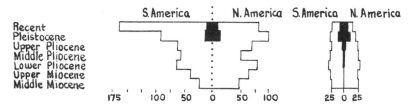

Fig. 38. Comparison of the mammal faunas of North and South America. *Black*: genera (left) and families (right) common to both areas. After data from Simpson.

evolution of the connection which did not become a continuous isthmus until late in the Neogene becomes evident from a comparison of the two faunas (Fig. 38). Migration appears to have been mainly from north to south. As might be expected the fauna of the isthmus itself is a mixture of North and South American elements with no endemic species.

An example of a " sweepstakes route " is found between Asia and Australia. A continuous land-bridge never existed here in the Cainozoic, and only a very small part of the fauna was able to utilise this inadequate route. Simpson assumes that it was purely by accident that primitive marsupials reached Australia first and subsequently evolved there, filling ecological niches which were occupied by placentals elsewhere in the world (herbivores, insectivores and carnivores). The old popular general assumption that the marsupials must have reached Australia at a time when the connection was better, and that this connection resolved itself into an island chain before the evolution of the placental mammals began, has become much less likely since it became known that both groups already existed in the Cretaceous and probably represent contemporaneous divergences in the early evolution of the mammals.

Connections which varied in the extent they could be used appear to have existed during the course of the Cainozoic between Eurasia and Africa and between Asia and North America. This implies that all the continents must have been connected directly or indirectly. The degree of faunal relationship between them is important. What is immediately noticeable is that the New World's position is far less isolated than might be supposed. There is an obvious relationship between the mammalian faunas of North America and Asia. In contrast the relationship between North America and Europe is slight, while the forms they have in common all occur in Asia. This makes it clear, beyond all doubt, that Europe and North America were connected via Asia and the connection must have been in the region of the present Bering Strait. Leaving aside Australia for the moment, the continents can be arranged in a chain: South America, North America, Asia, Europe, Africa. It is well known that the faunal relationship between two regions decreases with the distance, and this is the case in the chain of continents. The two continents with the smallest measure of relationship are South America and Africa. At the level of genera their faunas do not have a single corresponding element in the Cainozoic. There is a slight amount of correspondence in the higher categories. It follows from this that South America and Africa must be regarded as the ends of the chain: their only connection ran via the Bering Strait. If a shorter connection had existed in the Cainozoic it would have been revealed in a greater degree of faunal relationship. In other words, the most important line of demarcation for the continental mammalian fauna of the Cainozoic is the Atlantic Ocean. Simpson therefore concludes that the present pattern of continents and oceans gives a perfectly satisfactory explanation of the distribution of the Cainozoic mammals (Fig. 39).

An abundance of data has gradually been collected about the reptiles which would make them prime material on which to base a study of the earlier history of continental vertebrate fauna in the Mesozoic and the Upper Palaeozoic. Equally valuable information about the Mesozoic can, however, be obtained from primitive mammals, while amphibians and fish also provide relevant data, especially for the Palaeozoic. The point is all the more interesting as conflicting views are held. In a detailed study Joleaud (1923) advanced numerous arguments, especially those based on the

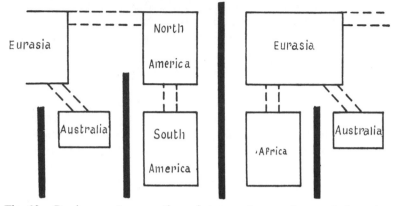

Fig. 39. Barriers and connections between the continents during the Cainozoic. After Simpson.

reptiles, in support of the concept of continental drift in the sense in which it was understood by Wegener. Although more recent evidence has sometimes refuted these arguments, it cannot be denied that there is often a remarkable relationship among the Upper Palaeozoic and Mesozoic faunas on the various continents. The Crossopterygii, for example, had a global distribution at their peak in the Upper Devonian. Many genera are known in different continents, especially Europe and North America, a fact which is difficult to comprehend without the assumption of land bridges. In this connection it is important to note that many European and North American genera are also found in Greenland. The same applies to the first quadruped land animals which appear simultaneously in various regions. Similar correspondences in continental vertebrate faunas are known throughout the whole of the Upper Palaeozoic and the Mesozoic; the question is not so much whether a particular relationship exists between the faunas of the various continents but rather in what degree it is present. Simpson's study of the mammals has convincingly demonstrated that faunal similarities are also possible and comprehensible in the present pattern of continents and oceans. In order to visualise the connections which are zoogeographically desirable, quantitative data concerning the measure of relationship must be available. The continental faunas of the Upper Palaeozoic and the Mesozoic have not so far been studied from this angle.

5. Continental floras

Continental floras form a special problem. The manner in which they are spread resembles in principle the way in which sessile benthonic animals are spread in the sea. Both live attached to their environment, so that their potential for distribution is dependent on a free "embryonic" stage, represented in the plants by seed or spores. Their distribution is determined by whether they land in a place where germination is ecologically possible. Their rate of distribution depends on the distance over which seeds and spores are dispersed, possibly by running water or by animals, and on the time needed to reproduce seeds and spores; 10-20 years is necessary for some trees to accomplish this.

Too little is known of Lower Palaeozoic and Devonian floras for even an approximate reconstruction of their distribution pattern. Many more facts are available for the Lower Carboniferous. Although a few plants in this period had a limited distribution, the flora as a whole displayed very little geographical differentiation.

The Upper Carboniferous and the Permian, however, present an entirely different picture. In the first place there appeared to have been a clear differentiation between the continents of the northern and southern hemispheres. Asia south of the Himalayas should be included in the latter as is often the case in contexts other than palaeontological. In the second place there appeared to have been a further differentiation, albeit a less sharp one, within the northern hemisphere.

In the southern hemisphere the flora displayed a very uniform character, with numerous closely related or possibly even corresponding forms. The term Glossopteris flora, named after its most characteristic components, is used, although the designation Gondwana flora is preferable as the genus *Glossopteris* itself is not present everywhere. It is hardly remarkable that this flora with its homogeneous composition in southern South America, Africa, India, Australia and Antarctica (Fig. 40) has been brought into the discussion of continental drift from the start. It would be rash, however, to see in the uniform character of the flora of this period a proof of an enclosed Gondwana continent, as it is known that much later, in the Miocene and the Pliocene, and even in the Pleistocene when the pattern of continents and oceans was undoubtedly similar to the present arrangement, various genera, among them *Nothofagus*, showed a similar distribution.

In contrast with the homogeneous character of the Gondwana, the northern flora had greater differentiation. Three floras can be distinguished:

(*i*) the Euro-American flora, known in Greenland and North Africa as well as in Europe and North America

(*ii*) the Angara flora, chiefly in Siberia, and

(*iii*) the Cathaysia flora, which occurs in South East Asia and also in south-western North America.

Of these three the Angara flora is the most distinctive; the other two exhibit greater mutual similarity and occur together in a part of North America. The Cathaysia flora penetrated southwards between the Gondwana flora of India and Australia to Malaya and Sumatra, but only in New Guinea did it appear together with *Glossopteris*. Northern elements are also known to have come into contact with the Gondwana flora in South America and South Africa, while *Glossopteris* appears to have occurred in the Urals. In spite of the individual character of these floras there were apparently no impenetrable barriers which could impede their distribution into other floral provinces.

Although the Gondwana flora gradually changed in composition in the Trias, it retained its distinctiveness, and differed in character from the northern floras. These differences, however, became steadily less apparent and in the Jurassic the flora had an astonishing uniformity from Greenland to Grahamland, and from North America to Japan.

The pattern becomes less distinct with the appearance of angiosperm flora in the Upper Cretaceous. During the Cainozoic an increasing measure of differentiation becomes apparent, primarily in the development of climatological zones. This process reached a culminating point in the Pleistocene.

The Pleistocene period possessed many phytogeographically interesting characteristics; it had a peculiar climate, and its many well-known floras, due to their close relationship with recent floras, provided a reliable basis for ecological and climatological interpretation. Two phenomena are immediately obvious: (*i*) the massive and rapid migrations, especially in Europe and North America and (*ii*) the extinction of many Pliocene genera and the decrease in the

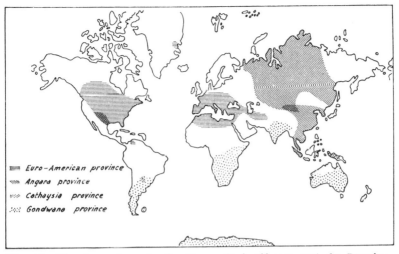

Fig. 40.   Floral provinces in the Upper Carboniferous and the Permian.
After Gothan and Weyland.

range of others which led to a noticeable impoverishment of the
flora, particularly in Europe. The migrations were linked with the
alternate expansion and melting of the great Pleistocene ice-caps,
and possessed a scope and tempo unequalled in the earlier history
of the Earth. The climatologically determined vegetation belts
often shifted southwards with the ice, so that in a large part of
Central and Western Europe the vegetation alternated between
Arctic tundra and temperate deciduous forest. The natural reaffores-
tation that has taken place since the last glacial period has been
particularly well studied, so that it is possible to indicate the places
where many elements found refuge from the ice and the migration
routes along which they returned: the latter process has been made
feasible by pollen analysis. The large number of well dated pollen
diagrams available makes it possible to trace the stages in the
spread of many trees in space as well as in time. The glacial refuges
of the post-glacial immigrants lay in South West and South East
Europe. Because of the crescent shape of the Alpine system no
room was left in Central Europe between the southern edge of the
Scandinavian land ice and these young fold mountains for species
that needed a temperate climate. They died out in this region north
of the Pyrenees, the Alps and the Carpathians. In the course of

the Pleistocene a gradual impoverishment of the Western European flora can be observed, fewer species returning after each glaciation. Many trees and shrubs which were normal elements in the Western European flora in the Pliocene or the beginning of the Pleistocene are still found in South East Asia and elsewhere. Ecologically, some of these could have thrived here in the interglacial conditions of the Holocene, but geographically the region was inaccessible. Many of the ornamental shrubs and trees in parks and gardens prove that some of these species are able to grow in Western Europe if they are introduced artificially. In North America, where the most important mountain chains run from north to south and not from east to west, the interaction of the climate of the Pleistocene and the topography has had much less serious consequences. There were fewer obstacles to hamper the southward retreat in a glacial period, and a much greater part of the flora was able to spread northwards again during each interglacial phase.

CHAPTER 4

THE VERTICAL DISTRIBUTION OF FOSSILS
(STRATIGRAPHICAL PALAEONTOLOGY)

1. *The vertical classification of sedimentary successions*

A vertical sequence of sedimentary rocks can be classified in a number of ways. Apart from clearly recognisable interruptions in sedimentation, the field geologist first makes use of the lithology. He distinguishes sandstones, limestones, shales and other sediments as components of the sequence in question. If he is experienced he will be able to introduce further refinement into his field-classification by noting the mineralogical character of the sandstones, their grain size and the rounding of the component minerals, the character of the limestones, and many other properties which the practical geologist can observe with no other equipment than a hand lens. On this basis, the first phase of the work of any geologist in a new region, it is possible to make a certain stratigraphical classification in the field. As the distinction of the components and the classification of the sequence is based on the lithological properties of the sediment, the result is termed a lithostratigraphy. This stratigraphy is complete in itself and initially it need not have any connection with the general stratigraphical scale.

To the same category, in principle, belong those classifications that are also dependent on lithological characteristics, but cannot be established until further research has been carried out with the help of more complicated apparatus in laboratories or boreholes. Such classifications include those based on the quantitative distribution of heavy minerals, the electrical properties of the sediments, radioactivity, and on boring speed and many other of the techniques applied in modern subsurface geology. Although it is true that, from the purely scientific viewpoint, these techniques are not valued equally everywhere—Jeletzky (1956) speaks of " technologically glorified stratigraphy "—this in no way diminishes the fact that they constitute a certain type of lithostratigraphy.

The fundamental lithostratigraphical unit is the formation. Two or more formations together may form a group. The term formation is still used as a synonym for system in a number of countries. As synonyms should be avoided in scientific terminology, formation will be used here in its lithostratigraphical sense—a usage which is recommended by the International Subcommission on Stratigraphic Terminology (Hedberg, chairman, 1961) and by the American Commission on Stratigraphic Nomenclature. Parts of a formation can be referred to as members, or, depending on their shape, tongues or lenses. It should be pointed out that even a smaller lithostratigraphical unit is not necessarily lithologically homogeneous. A rhythmic, alternating sequence of two or more lithological units can serve as the characteristic feature of a lithostratigraphical unit.

A sedimentary sequence can be classified according to its organic character (its fossil content) as well as on the basis of its inorganic characters (its lithology). The term biostratigraphy is then used on the analogy of lithostratigraphy. In the light of modern views concerning the basis of stratigraphy this is not just the only meaningful, but also the most logical, significance of the term.

In Chapter 2 it was seen that the presence of fossils in a deposit is sometimes the result of transport and sedimentation. If fossils, along with mineral particles, are regarded as an integral part of a sediment—a part that is sometimes missing, and sometimes the main component—then there remains in principle no obvious distinction between lithostratigraphy and biostratigraphy. Both are based on objective criteria. In one respect, however, there is a difference: an alternation of sandstones and shales may occur at any moment in the history of the earth, but a sequence of fossil species is associated with a particular time. This is because organic evolution, in contrast to inorganic development, never repeats itself.

For present purposes it will be assumed that biostratigraphy is independent of a world wide division of sedimentary rocks based on their time of formation. The relationship of lithostratigraphy and biostratigraphy to chronostratigraphy will be examined in Section 5.

2. *The zone as a biostratigraphical unit*

Any part of a sedimentary succession which is distinguished by all or part of the fossil species preserved in it, is a biostratigraphical unit. For more than a century the term zone in one context or another has been used as the fundamental unit in biostratigraphy. This use of the word zone originated with A. Oppel (1831-1865) and it has been accepted as a stratigraphical term on a number of occasions by International Geological Congresses.

Oppel studied the Jurassic not only of southern Germany, but also that of England, France and Switzerland. He saw that certain strata, or groups of strata, could be recognised from their fossils over large and even widely separated areas. In his major work, *Die Juraformation Englands, Frankreichs und des südwestlichen Deutschlands* (1856-58) (The Jurassic system of England, France and S.W. Germany), he used the term zone for such parts of a sedimentary sequence. This term was not new; in France d'Orbigny (1802-1857) had also made use of it, especially when speaking of the vertical distribution of fossils in his *étages,* but its meaning was not precise. It is remarkable that Oppel did not define the term. He used it so carefully and consistently, however, that there can be no doubt that for him the zone meant a scrupulously defined stratigraphical unit.

Ever since Oppel's time the Jurassic system has been a favourite subject for detailed stratigraphical research, the ammonites being the fossils characteristic of the zones. Fig. 41 shows the vertical distribution of the ammonites in one part of the southern English Jurassic. By way of comparison Fig. 42 shows a Palaeozoic example, namely the vertical distribution of the zone graptolites of the Ordovician and the Silurian.

Certain general observations arise from a study of these and many other examples of the vertical distribution of fossils. The first, and most immediately apparent, is that the zones seldom occur as natural units.

A zone can be characterised by an association of fossil species, or by a single species, a genus or other taxon. Accordingly two principal kinds of biostratigraphic units can be recognised, the assemblage-zone or cenozone, and the range-zone or acrozone. The definition of an assemblage-zone should include a compre-

9

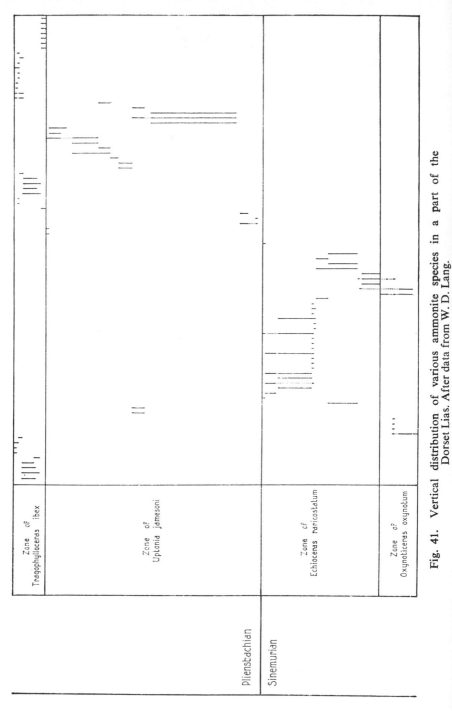

Fig. 41. Vertical distribution of various ammonite species in a part of the Dorset Lias. After data from W. D. Lang.

Zone of
Tragophylloceras ibex

Zone of
Uptonia jamesoni

Zone of
Echioceras raricostatum

Zone of
Oxynoticeras oxynotum

Pliensbachian

Sinemurian

Fig. 42. Vertical distribution of zone graptolites in the Ordovician and Silurian of Great Britain. After data from Elles.

123

hensive description of the fossil assemblage and its diagnostic elements. Usually the zone is named after one or two of these diagnostic elements. Recently the International Subcommission on Stratigraphic Terminology (Hedberg, chairman, 1961) also suggested that a specifically designated and delimited type section, or reference section, should be included in any proposal to establish a named assemblage-zone. An assemblage-zone may be subdivided into assemblage-subzones. If still smaller units can be distinguished the term assemblage-zonule is available. The principal standard of reference of a range-zone is the biological concept of the particular taxon (species, genus, etc.) on which it is based.

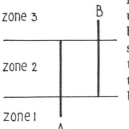

Fig. 43. Schematic example of the characterisation of a zone by a combination of two species.

Two other kinds of biostratigraphic units should be mentioned here. The first one is the epibole, also called acme-zone or peak-zone, which corresponds with the strata representing the maximum development of some species, genus or other taxon. Although in some cases such a unit may suffer from a certain vagueness as to what constitutes " maximum development", in other cases it may represent a convenient practical unit. Like the range-zone the epibole takes its name from the taxon whose zone of maximum development it delimits.

A special kind of range-zone results from the concurrence or overlap in range of two, or even more taxa (Fig. 43). The American Stratigraphic Commission adopted the term concurrent-range zone for this biostratigraphical unit. If the particular taxa are well chosen it may constitute a significant and useful unit.

The delimitation of zones is partly subjective; the personal preference and the experience of the investigator play some part in the matter. A research worker seldom arrives at the same classification of zones as his predecessor, even when starting out from the same material. This is clearly reflected in the continual revision of the zonal tables of intensively investigated stratigraphical units such as the Jurassic. Generally accepted zonal classifications often depend on the authority of a single investigator.

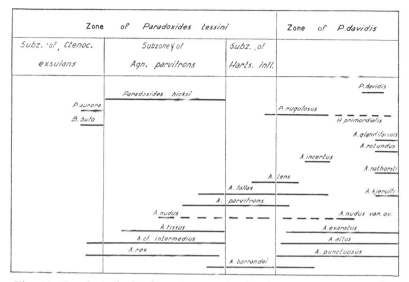

Fig. 44. Vertical distribution of zone trilobites in a part of the English
Middle Cambrian, the zonal classification of which is based on the Scandinavian Middle Cambrian. After Neaverson.

The artificial character of the zone becomes even more apparent
when two classifications, each based on a different group of fossils,
are made for the same larger stratigraphical unit. The zonal
boundaries in the two classifications do not generally coincide. This
phenomenon which is important both theoretically and practically
will be returned to later.

If a further inspection is made of Fig. 41, it will be seen that the
thickness of the zones in a given section may vary considerably.
This is not surprising because the actual thickness of a particular
section may be controlled not only by such palaeontological factors
as the tempo of evolutionary change, but also by the rate of sedimentation and the degree to which the environmental conditions
remain constant.

Even when all the the factors that influence the vertical distribution of fossils have been taken into consideration, the demarcation
of the zones may often remain rather vague. Every geologist knows
from experience that fossils are seldom found evenly distributed
throughout a sedimentary succession of any thickness but they are

often concentrated in definite layers. The demarcation of the zones, therefore, is also influenced by the actual distribution of fossils. In this respect it should also be borne in mind that the appearance of a species will provide a better criterion than its disappearance. The degree to which old forms maintain themselves is generally governed by more fortuitous factors than is the appearance of new forms.

It follows from the definition given above that the zone is not in principle a world-wide unit. The limits which ecological and geographical factors impose on the horizontal distribution of organisms also restrict the horizontal extent of the zone. The latter depends primarily, in relation to the ecological and geographical factors that govern its distribution, on the group which provides the zone fossils. Oppel realised that his classification of the zones of the Jurassic, based on ammonites, was applicable to much of Western Europe. But although various zone ammonites have a considerable distribution, it is still not possible to apply this Western European zonal classification in the Near East, for example. There a classification on different lines is necessary to facilitate a comparison with Western Europe and other regions.

Zones can equally well be intercontinental in extent. It is becoming increasingly apparent that the goniatite zones of the marine Carboniferous, and the plant zones of the continental Carboniferous in Western Europe and in North America, display the same sequence. The Ordovician and Silurian graptolites provide an example of a group of zone fossils which combine a large geographical distribution with a limited ecological one. The graptolite zones which are based on the sequence in the Caledonian geosyncline are found in a large area of Europe including the Ardennes and the Montagne Noire, but on the borders of the Caledonian geosyncline they are so rare that they lose all significance as zone fossils.

The definitions of the several kinds of biostratigraphical zones give no information about the relationship between zonal and chronological boundaries; in other words, a zone is not necessarily of equal age throughout its extent. Consequently a zone is nearer, in this respect, to being a lithostratigraphical unit than a chronostratigraphical unit. It is useful to draw attention to this point at this stage; but in the latter part of this chapter there will be ⌐

more detailed discussion of the relationship between lithostratigraphical and biostratigraphical units on the one hand, and
chronostratigraphical units on the other.

Both before and after Oppel, geologists have used the term
zone as a stratigraphical concept. Although the International Geological Congresses have on more than one occasion made good
Oppel's failure to define the term, there has always been a group
of geologists who regard the zone as a chronological unit. This
is not only in conflict with the original use of the term and with
subsequent international agreements, but also a regrettable confusion of stratigraphical and chronological units which in this case
is all the more serious, as it has been seen that the zone cannot
be considered *a priori* as the chronostratigraphical equivalent of
a time unit.

Summarising, it can only be concluded that the zone concept
represents an area fraught with difficulties. Remarkably this does
not detract from the practical usefulness of the different kinds of
zones as elementary stratigraphical units. A comparison with the
species concept in systematics is almost inevitable; the analogy is
not altogether fortuitous. Both concepts are concerned with the
classification of material without natural breaks. In the one case
it is the whole organic world whose various members are connected through an infinite number of transitions, in the other it
is the sedimentary sequence, which is the reflection of continuous
time.

3. *Stages and higher chronostratigraphical units*

In contrast to the zone, the stage is a chronostratigraphical unit,
and this in itself labels it as a world-wide unit. By definition a
stage is bounded on its upper and lower sides by isochronous
planes: the sediments in all parts of the world which were formed
in the same period of time should be included in the same stage.

The term age is used as the chronological equivalent of the
stratigraphical stage. It would have been better to use some term
for this very specialised meaning which was not in current use, in a
more neutral sense, both in everyday life and in geology.

There is no uniform system of stage nomenclature in use throughout the world. In the first place there are numerous current syno-

nyms which would be invalid if there were a system of rules for stratigraphical nomenclature such as exists for the nomenclature of plants and animals. This, unfortunately, is not the case. In addition to the 11 Jurassic stages which he recognised as valid, Arkell has discovered in Western Europe alone more than 100 synonymous names that have been proposed in the course of time for Jurassic stratigraphy. Secondly every region which more or less comprises a geological entity often has its own system of stage names. This can be explained historically, but it would be incorrect to assume that this state of affairs is maintained solely for the sake of tradition. Replacement by a uniform system implies careful correlations, but these are often surrounded by considerable practical difficulties. In theory it should be possible to have a single uniform system of stage names for the whole world. Arkell's *Jurassic geology of the world* (1956) attempted a general application of the standard classification of the Jurassic stages which are based on Western Europe.

Although in theory the concept of the stage seems to be both simple and sound, in practice it presents many problems. The difficulties are increased because the stage, as the basic working unit of chronostratigraphical classification, forms the basis of the whole chronostratigraphical system and consequently geochronology. A stage should be based on a specifically designated and delimited type section. In the type section its upper and lower boundary may or may not coincide with boundaries between other kinds of stratigraphical units, such as lithostratigraphical or biostratigraphical units. If such a coincidence exists in the type section it does not necessarily exist at other localities away from the type section, a stage being bounded by isochronous planes. The latter may cut across boundaries based on lithological or palaeontological characteristics of the succession. Consequently outside the type section a stage, or any other chronostratigraphical unit, is not as easily recognised as lithostratigraphical or biostratigraphic units based on observable features.

Usually the name of a stage is derived from a geographical name occurring in the area of the type section. Arkell has proposed that this should be made a general rule as soon as a system of rules for stratigraphical nomenclature comes into being. Such formally recognised stage names should preferably have an " ian " or " an " ending. For clarity the term " stage " may be added where desirable.

It follows from what has been said that the usefulness of the concept of the stage is intimately connected with the problem of chronostratigraphical correlation, a point which will be explored in the next section.

The difficulties connected with such correlations are encountered not only when transferring established stage names from one region to another, but also when formulating a closed system of stages. In a complete system there should be no overlapping and no gaps. If a complete system were based on a continuous sequence no difficulties would arise, but as no such sequence exists, completeness can only be achieved through combining various sections. For historical reasons most stages are based in Western Europe, which does not always form an ideal starting point. The three highest stages of the Cretaceous provide an instructive example of this. The Campanian, the Maastrichtian and the Danian are based on sections which are 500-600 kilometres apart. It cannot be expected that what is regarded on the northern edge of the Aquitanian Basin as the upper limit of the Campanian should correspond with what is considered at the foot of the Ardennes as the lower limit of the Maastrichtian, nor that the upper limit there of the Maastrichtian should in turn correspond with what is taken as the lower limit of the Danian in Denmark.

In all such cases where successive stages are based on various sections, the drawing of satisfactory boundaries is only possible through mutual discussion and after careful research. This means that secondary characters which perhaps were not included in the original definition of a stage should be considered as an essential part of the definition.

What holds good for stages must also apply *mutatis mutandis* to all higher stratigraphical categories: series, systems and erastems. There is the theoretical difference that units above the rank of stage can be defined by means of the stages belonging to them. As long as there is no uniform system of stages in use, this procedure must remain rather dubious. There are also differences of opinion about the placing of stages within the higher categories. A classic example of this is the placing of the Rhaetian either as the highest stage of the Trias or as the lowest stage of the Jurassic. There are arguments for both points of view. It is remarkable that in such a longstanding difference of opinion the palaeontological character of the Rhaetian in the type area has never been taken into consideration. In 1956 Arkell drew attention to the fact that the ammonite fauna of the Rhaetian in the Rhaetic Alps has a definitely Triassic character, and shows hardly any Jurassic affinities. This is a reasonable argument and much more valuable than earlier ones based on the lithological similarity of the Rhaetian to the Upper Trias, on the absence of ammonites, or on the fact that the Rhaetian forms the beginning of the Jurassic transgression. Arkell (1955, p. 38) wrote ". . . and consequently the Rhaetic Beds are here regarded as belonging to the Triassic System." 23 years earlier it was: " It is now generally agreed that the Rhaetic Beds are best classed as the basal member of the Jurassic System. . . . There is no datum so suitable for starting the Jurassic System as that marked by the Rhaetic Transgression, the effects of which are marked all over North-West Europe " (Arkell, 1933, p. 97).

Similar differences of opinion also exist concerning the arrangement of higher units. In England it has long been customary to regard the Tremadocian as the highest series of the Cambrian, since it is divided from the Arenigian which follows it by a small unconformity. The fauna of the Tremadocian, however, has a clearly Ordovician character. In countries such as Norway and France, where the unconformity between Tremadocian and Arenigian is insignificant, and where this typical field geologist's physical boundary is lacking, the Tremadocian is regarded as the lowest series of the Ordovician.

The English Downtonian cannot be altogether equated with the Gedinnian of the Belgian and French geologists, but the two do partly correspond: they could not both be given a place in a chronostratigraphical scale. In England the Downtonian, with its alternation of marine and continental sediments, constitutes the final phase of the infilling in the Caledonian geosyncline and therefore is considered as the highest part of the Silurian. Similarly in the southern Ardennes the Gedinnian represents the beginning of the sedimentation in the Variscan geosyncline, and consequently the base of the Devonian. In this case the difficulties are further increased by the fact that marine fossils are of little importance in the two sections. A practicable boundary would therefore have to be based on a complete marine transition from Silurian to Devonian deposits. As long as no standard section of this type is available, the boundary will remain somewhat arbitrary.

A good example of the manner in which chronostratigraphical boundaries might be fixed is provided by that between the Pliocene and the Pleistocene. The 18th International Geological Congress held in London in 1948 indicated a region where this transition took place in marine deposits as a type area, and fixed the boundary so that the Calabrian, where a definite cooling of the climate is first reflected, represents the lowest Pleistocene. Palaeontological criteria indirectly determine the boundary, as this is based on a marine sequence with marine fossils and the palaeoclimate is deduced from the fauna. This decision of the congress, however, says nothing about the placing of the boundary outside the type area. The application of the accepted boundary in other areas is a matter for scientific investigation and not for a congress resolution.

In spite of the success of this attempt to achieve greater uniformity of usage in one particular case, it is doubtful whether a decision by an international congress is the best procedure for solving the many cases in which there are differences of opinion about the placing of stratigraphical boundaries. Many geologists believe that it would be much more desirable to agree first on rules for stratigraphical nomenclature. A great many of the problems would probably then be solved simply by applying those rules. Arkell (1946) has already made a number of suggestions for such rules and many more are to be found in the publications of the American Commission on Stratigraphic Nomenclature, especially its Code of Stratigraphic Nomenclature (*Bull. Am. Ass. Petrol. Geol.*, 1961, **45,** 645-660) and the statement of Principles of Stratigraphic Classification and Terminology, by the International Subcommission on Stratigraphic Terminology (*Int. geol. Congr.,* 21. Copenhagen, 1961, **25,** 7-16).

Does all this imply that most of the higher units have no biostratigraphical meaning? It is certainly true that most of them have been introduced in a fairly arbitrary manner, and that originally they were usually based on other than palaeontological criteria. Initially, lithological and tectonic data perhaps had a greater influence. Many higher units, especially systems, however,

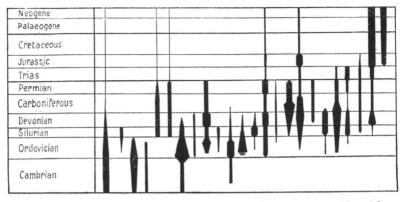

Fig. 45.   Stratigraphical distribution of the brachiopod superfamilies. After
Shrock and Twenhofel.

have had their boundaries revised in the course of time in order
to eliminate gaps between the units and to make their demarcation clearer (Figs. 45, 46). Although most system boundaries have
since been defined palaeontologically, there exist great differences
in the palaeontological significance of these demarcations. The
stratigraphy of the Mesozoic is largely based on ammonites. The
boundary between the Trias (including the Rhaetian) and the
Jurassic appears a very clear demarcation from the point of view
of ammonite palaeontology. Only one superfamily (Fig. 47) sur-
vived the transition from Trias to Jurassic, so that the development
of the rich ammonite fauna of the latter period stems from this
one group. In contrast the boundary between the Jurassic and the
Cretaceous is less sharply defined, while the upper boundary of
the Cretaceous has in general no significance from the point of view
of ammonite palaeontology, as can be seen from Fig. 47. The
impression cannot be avoided that when Désor in 1846 incorpo-
rated his new stage, the Danian, in the Cretaceous, he did so
exclusively on the basis of the lithological development. Palaeontologically there is much to be said for including the Danian in
the Palaeogene, which would result in the boundary between the
Mesozoic and the Cainozoic coinciding with the upper limit of
the Maastrichtian.

Remarkably enough not only is the Mesozoic-Cainozoic boundary somewhat vague, but also that between the Palaeozoic and

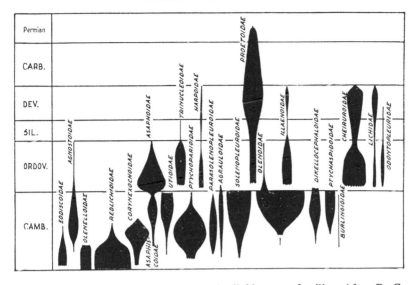

Fig. 46. Stratigraphical distribution of trilobite superfamilies. After R. C. Moore.

the Mesozoic. Throughout the whole of Western Europe this boundary is based on a sequence in which marine deposits are very scarce. It is a typical example of a boundary that could have been better defined in some other area. It is consequently no accident that the justification of the existence of the Permian as an independent entity should have been disputed more often than that of any other system.

The Permian reveals another aspect of the nature of the higher units. Due to the strong development of the continental deposits in this period, the Permian flora as well as Upper Carboniferous ones are well known. For practical reasons all the boundaries are based on marine invertebrates but it would be equally possible in some cases to use continental floras. If these are brought in to aid the definition of the Permian boundary, two points emerge. Firstly, there is much to be said for drawing the Carboniferous-Permian boundary not between the Stephanian and the Autunian, but at the top of the Autunian. Secondly, the Permian is not florally a very homogeneous entity. The boundary between the Palaeozoic and the Mesozoic may be rather vague, but the con-

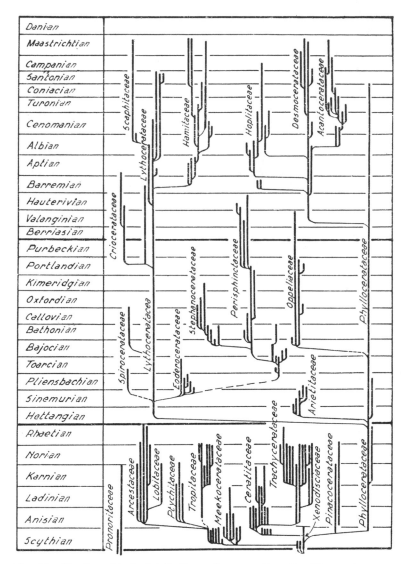

Fig. 47. Stratigraphical distribution of ammonites (families and super-families) in the Mesozoic. After R. C. Moore.

trast between their marine invertebrate faunas is clear enough. Some groups, such as the rugose and tabulate corals, and the trilobites, disappear from the scene: other groups which have already been present on a modest scale expand and begin a new chapter in their evolution. The same applies to the flora, but if a distinction is made between the Palaeozoic and Mesozoic floras, it will be seen that the boundary does not coincide with that between the corresponding faunas. It has to be placed a little earlier, between what is usually termed in Western Europe the Lower Permian (Rotliegende) and the Upper Permian (Zechstein).

Rather similar considerations apply to the boundary between the " Mesophytic " and " Cainophytic ". The great expansion of the angiosperms clearly begins before the end of the Cretaceous. From the palaeobotanical viewpoint much of the Cretaceous belongs to the Cainozoic.

These points may serve as a reminder that stratigraphical boundaries do not demarcate natural entities, but merely make it easier to bring under survey the continuous time reflected in the sediments. This does not prevent evolution from appearing to move faster at some moments than at others, but even then transitions remain gradual. Abrupt transitions only occur when the sequence is incomplete. Such sequences, however much they may have been used in the past, are not a suitable base for a general stratigraphic system because they constitute an incomplete representation of time. The more fully time is reflected in a sequence, the hazier the boundaries will be. Although most units at the level of the system are palaeontologically defined with some degree of sharpness, their palaeontological coating is so thin sometimes that it barely conceals the original nature of the unit.

4. Correlations

A correlation exists between two strata when they have certain characters in common. Since a stratum, or a group of strata, can seldom be traced over a long distance without interruption, every geological interpretation must rest on the recognition of correlated strata. This applies equally well to the reconstruction of the infilling of a sedimentary basin as, for example, to the interpretation of a tectonic structure. No sedimentary basin actually appears in the field in the way in which it is ultimately represented in a number of maps and sections. Such a representation is based on a comparison of the sedimentary sequence at as many points as possible. The greater the certainty with which correlations can be established, the more reliable the picture gained. The tracing of correlations is thus one of the most elementary and at the same time one of the most fundamental tasks of the geologist.

Just as there are various possible classifications of a sedimentary sequence, different correlations are possible. A correspondence in lithological composition leads to the recognition of a lithological correlation. Similarly there are biostratigraphical correlations based on the correspondence of palaeontological characters, and chronostratigraphical correlations based on corresponding times of formation.

The value of fossils for stratigraphical correlations was clearly recognised in the first half of the nineteenth century by researchers such as William Smith in England, Alcide d'Orbigny in France and Albert Oppel in Germany. These workers who were soon followed by many others rejected chronological correlations based on lithological correspondence. This was an important step forward, because a particular lithological sequence may repeat itself at any time in the history of the earth but the evolution of life is a process in which no repetitions occur. In this respect there is thus an essential difference between lithostratigraphical and biostratigraphical correlations.

Lithostratigraphical correlations have a relative value, their significance decreasing rapidly with increasing horizontal distance; but such a correlation between sections from two different continents may be significant if continental drift has subsequently occurred. A biostratigraphical correlation, however, is of the greatest importance in such an instance. If such a correlation exists between a section in Europe and one in America, because, for example, representatives of the Archaeocythacea appear in both, then a very important fact has been established. Even when the species, or even the genera, do not correspond, and in fact they rarely do in this group, the two sections concerned can be ascribed to the Cambrian.

The detailed palaeontological comparison of two different sections often presents the investigator with all kinds of difficulties.

Even apart from differences resulting from ecological and geographical factors, a direct comparison is rarely possible. Fig. 48 represents this in diagram form. Section A and section B both consist of a sequence of limestone, shale and limestone which could thus provide the basis for a lithostratigraphical comparison. If only B were available, then in practice the transition from shale to limestone would also serve as the boundary between the local range zones of the forms 5 and 7. In A, however, this lithological boundary lies in the middle of the local range zone 5.

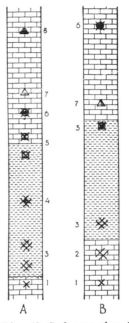

In one aspect Fig. 48 departs from reality; usually there is not a simple sequence of species but a sequence of faunas. Even if this increases the possibilities of making biostratigraphical correlations, it also makes the zoning of two or more sections difficult since the ranges of the different faunal components rarely coincide. This introduces a subjective element that is hardly present in the case of Fig. 48. Two lines of approach are possible: either the fauna as a whole can be taken as a starting point; or a particular group can be chosen on which correlations

Fig. 48. Schematised palaeontological comparison of two sections.

may be based. The latter procedure is the more usual. A closer examination of the other groups present is often neglected, which may lead to incorrect conclusions both from the practical and the theoretical viewpoint (see Section 5). It is clear that detailed biostratigraphical correlations are based on the distinction of assemblage zones, or possibly assemblage subzones. Fig. 48 demonstrates that the drafting of a zonal classification in a single section is possible and often provides a starting point, but it also shows that a classification which is generally valid is only feasible after as many sections as possible have been compared. In Fig. 48 section A form 2 is missing, and in section B form 4, while a comparison of these two sections does not solve the question of the correct place of form 7 in relation to

10

5 and 6. This means that the formulation of a general zonal classification cannot be separated from the recognition of correlations. The number of sections to be compared increases considerably with the extent of the area for which the classification is valid, while the variations between the standard and the individual sections also increase. No standard section of the ammonite zones of Western Europe is fully developed in any of the classical Jurassic areas, because of gaps in the sequence and the absence of characteristic zone fossils in certain regions. The same applies to the Ordovician and Silurian graptolite zones.

The usefulness of biostratigraphical correlations by means of zones depends largely on the choice of zone fossils. The more strongly a group is tied to its environment, the more limited are the possibilities of applying correlations. Benthonic animals which are sensitive to bathymetric conditions are consequently less useful than pelagic forms. In this connection it is interesting to note that correlations based on ammonoids (Carboniferous, Permian, Trias, Jurassic and Cretaceous) or graptolites (Ordovician and Silurian) can more easily be applied over a large and even world-wide area, than those which are based, for example, on brachiopods or corals.

The value of fossils for tracing correlations increases as the rate of evolution of the group to which they belong increases. Consequently a particular group may have a different biostratigraphical value during different parts of its life span. Some groups experience more than one peak in their evolution. At such times new species follow each other in quick succession. The ammonoids are a group that is of the greatest biostratigraphical value throughout practically the whole of its history from the Devonian to the Cretaceous. If on the other hand the development of new species in a group takes place at a slow tempo, which is usually associated with a long species duration, then that group is of little biostratigraphical value, particularly when a high degree of subtlety is required in the correlations.

Geographical as well as ecological factors limit the distribution of organisms. Consequently no organism is distributed over the entire earth. This means that it is not possible to establish a system of direct biostratigraphical correlations to embrace the whole world. Direct correlations are only possible within an area which ecologically and geographically has the same faunal or floral character. The factors which restrict the horizontal extent of assemblage zones also limit biostratigraphical correlations. This correspondence is quite comprehensible if it is remembered that such a zone is characterised by a combination of fossils.

If because of ecological or geographical factors there is no general correspondence between the flora or fauna of two regions, other correlations must be sought. Several possibilities suggest themselves.

In the first place, it should be remembered that what constitutes an ecological or geographical boundary for one species is not necessarily a limit for another. Species which themselves are not suitable as zone fossils may have a distribution beyond the boundaries of the typical zone fossils. Such species are important in the approximate correlation of two areas with different zonal classifications.

When two areas with different faunas and floras are adjacent, the boundary between them does not remain constant for long. The dividing plane between the deposits of the one area and those of the other is consequently oblique and not vertical. It may be much more complicated as a result of the movements of the boundary. A boundary of this type appears in cross section as a zigzag line. Interfingering occurs between the two groups of deposits. It is important in tracing correlations between deposits with different faunas or floras, and naturally between deposits with different lithological characteristics. They demonstrate correlations which, in the boundary area at least, have chronostratigraphical value. Interfingering exists between sediments which differ in their fossil content both as a result of ecological and of geographical factors.

The correlation between the graptolite facies and the shelly facies in the Caledonian geosyncline is based on the interfingering of the two biotopes. In this case it is a question of two ecologically different marine environments, but there could be a much greater contrast between two environments. Interfingering is one of the most important phenomena used in the recognition of correlations between marine and continental areas. The correlation between the marine Carboniferous (goniatites) and the continental Carboniferous (plants and non-marine lamellibranchs) is apparent from the interfingering of the two, as in the marine bands of the paralic basins. An analogous example is found in some Pleistocene sedimentation areas, such as the North Sea basin, where marine deposits (with foraminifers, molluscs, etc.) and continental deposits (with mammals, molluscs and plants) interfringe. This makes it possible to compare the very important continental Pleistocene sequence which has a clear reflection of climatological fluctuations, with a perhaps less eloquent but more generally useful marine area.

It is more difficult to trace correlations between areas with different facies that have little or no contact with each other. An example of this is provided by a comparison of the Alpine and Germanic facies of the European Trias. The Germanic facies has a mainly continental character, only its middle part, the Muschelkalk, is marine. The Muschelkalk Sea, however, like the Zechstein Sea, represents a very specialised environment with an impoverished fauna. Because of the direct connection between the Muschelkalk Sea and the Mediterranean area, several elements from the latter area have penetrated some distance into the former, among them several species of *Ceratites,* and some lamellibranchs, including *Myophoria kefersteini.* It is these elements that make possible a limited comparison between the Alpine and Germanic facies.

In many cases a direct stratigraphical comparison between two areas is not possible. Some intermediary stage is then required. This is always necessary when it is a question of two areas which are not directly connected with one another, but even where this is not the case it can lead to useful results. Again the Trias provides a good example.

It has long been known that the remains of land plants are to be found both in the Alpine and the Germanic facies of the Trias, particularly the Upper Trias. These plants derive partly from the land area which separated the sedimentation basin of the Germanic Trias from the Tethys geosyncline; in other words they constitute the remains of the same floras as are found on both the southern edge of the Germanic and the northern edge of the Alpine area. This makes possible a comparison of the faunas of the Germanic and the Alpine facies, even although they do not have a single common element.

5. *The relationship between biostratigraphy and chronostratigraphy*

It is clear that no definite relationship exists between lithostratigraphy and chronostratigraphy. The lithological character of a deposit is determined by factors other than chronological ones: the upper and lower boundaries of a lithostratigraphical unit do not in general represent isochronous planes. The so-called " Lower Peat " which forms a well developed marker-horizon at the base of the Holocene on both sides of the North Sea yields a good example of a distinct lithostratigraphical unit bounded by diachronous planes. It was not formed at the same time throughout the whole of its area, but originated in a relatively narrow, marshy strip which was pushed continually landward by the transgression of the early Holocene sea. On the landward side of the strip, where peat was being formed at a particular time, there lay an area where peat had not yet been formed, while seaward peat formation had already been stopped by an overlying deposit of marine sediments. This pattern is confirmed by the fossil content of the peat, particularly the quantitative composition of the pollen which is a faithful reflection of climatological development during the Holocene. It should be remembered, however, that the absolute differences of age concerned here are very small in comparison with the length of the chronological unit with which the geologist generally deals. The difference in age of the Lower Peat in the west and east of Western Holland amounts to not more than a few thousand years. In the earlier Pleistocene, not to mention the Mesozoic and Palaeozoic, the tendency would be to regard an age difference of this order as an evidence of contemporaneity.

It is not difficult to imagine that under different circumstances a similar displacement of facies could occasion much greater time differences in the formation of a homogeneous lithostratigraphical unit. Geological literature contains many examples of this: the basal conglomerate of the Devonian in Belgium when traced from the south flank of the Dinant syncline to the north flank of the Namur syncline, shows an age difference equivalent to half the total Devonian period.

The recognition of chronostratigraphical units is a matter of which the significance can hardly be overestimated in an historical science such as geology. An historical synthesis, particularly one which aims at establishing causal connections, is only possible against the background of a uniform time scale. The history of ancient Egypt can be written in terms of the Egyptian dynasties and that of ancient China in terms of Chinese dynasties without troubling about the correlations between the two because no observable causal connection exists. In the history of the Earth's crust this approach is not possible because of the existence of many factors which operate on a world-wide scale. It has already been shown that even within a very limited area obtaining a logical picture of events is dependent on the recognition of correct chronological relationships.

It must be emphasised that there are very few stratigraphical planes or levels of a chronologically durable nature that are immediately recognisable as such. Over a very small distance a bedding plane and a stratum can be regarded as running parallel with isochronous planes, but over longer distances bedding planes cannot be traced, and this supposition does not hold good. A shifting of the facies will generally cause a stratum to intersect the isochronous planes, and the more closely a particular stratum is associated with a particular, clearly defined environment, the greater the likelihood of there being such an intersection. A comparison of the lithological and palaeontological characteristics of the deposit throws light on this. Conversely, deposits which originated virtually independently of the general environmental conditions are more useful as guides to chronology. This is sometimes the case with strata of volcanic ash, for example, and to a lesser extent with glacial deposits. It should be borne in mind that a deposit may embrace a smaller interval of time at the periphery of its area than in its central parts, so that the upper and lower surfaces may intersect isochronous planes although the stratum as a whole does not. Marine strata that are the result of transgressions of short duration also have a certain value as chronological indicators, as exemplified by the marine bands in the paralic Upper Carboniferous basins of Western Europe. Their shallow water origins, their large horizontal extent and their fixed place in the continental sequence make it reasonable to regard them as chronostratigraphical units.

Apart from incidental cases such as these, however, the geologist has no chronostratigraphical points of attachment at his disposal. The time chart of the historian is of no help because physical age determinations are too scarce to give stratigraphy its desired chronological background. In the absence of a physical scale recourse has to be found in a relative one.

It has already been shown that lithological evolution has no direct connection in principle with time. Biological evolution on the other hand is a function of time. The nature of this function will be examined in more detail in the next chapter. Although this function is not constant, this does not detract from the usefulness of biological evolution as a chronostratigraphical basis. Organic evolution is known from the palaeontological content of deposits from the past. This content, however, is not exclusively the result of organic evolution. It is also affected by ecological and geographical factors. In many cases, the time necessary for a species to spread from the locality where it evolved to other areas may be neglected. Unless there are geographical obstacles to distribution, the time needed even to reach distant regions is very small in comparison to the periods of time with which geology usually deals. For units of short duration, such as the subdivisions of the Pleistocene, this may not apply, but to take migration time into account for earlier and longer units would be to imply an accuracy that was unrealistic in comparison with other factors.

Ecological and geographical factors may hinder the distribution of a species or fauna, producing a geologically observable difference between the time of its first appearance at two points. Two examples will illustrate this.

In his classical investigations into the biostratigraphy of the Lower Carboniferous in the neighbourhood of Bristol, Vaughan relied on two groups of fossils, namely brachiopods and corals. He established that the sequence of brachiopod and of coral zones over a larger area corresponded in detail with those in the section along the Avon on which the investigations had originally been based. The relative position of the brachiopod and the coral zones appeared, however, to have shifted. To the north the coral zones came to lie higher stratigraphically in comparison to the brachiopod zones (Fig. 49). Similarly to the south the brachiopod zones became lower with respect to the coral zones. Only the relative shift emerges from the observations. What the absolute significance of the shift is with regard to chronostratigraphy is not immediately clear, although it can obviously be assumed that the coral faunas, with their greater ecological sensitivity, lagged behind the brachiopod faunas in their distribution. Whatever the explanation of the phenomenon may be, it appears sufficiently clear that at least one of the two zonal classifications has no chronostratigraphical value.

The second example is borrowed from Jeletzky's work on the Boreal Upper Cretaceous of Eurasia. While a clear distinction exists in the Santonian and the Lower Campanian between the Russian and the Western European parts of the Boreal province (characterised respectively by *Belemnitella* and *Gonioteuthis*), it can be

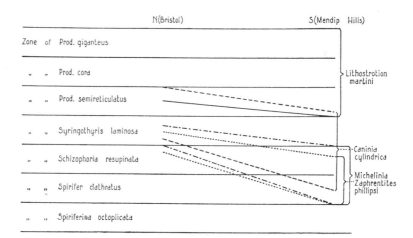

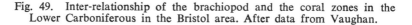

Fig. 49. Inter-relationship of the brachiopod and the coral zones in the Lower Carboniferous in the Bristol area. After data from Vaughan.

seen that in the transition to the Upper Campanian the whole Boreal área obtained a very uniform belemnite fauna, with *Belemnitella* as the dominant form. On the transition from Campanian to Maastrichtian the genus *Belemnella* appears as a new element in the Central Russian area. It quickly supplanted the genus *Belemnitella* in this subprovince, but in the remaining part of the Boreal province *Belemnella* did not gain this dominant position everywhere. In one part of the southern subprovince *Belemnitella* and *Belemnella* both occur in the Maastrichtian while still further south, in the Aquitanian Basin for example, *Belemnella* did not appear at all. The simultaneous presence of *Belemnella* and *Belemnitella* in one part of the southern subprovince is not an isolated phenomenon, because it is just here that Mediterranean elements, such as corals and rudists, appear as part of the fauna

of the Boreal region, Jeletzky believes therefore that the stratigraphical and geographical distribution of *Belemnitella* after the
Campanian has been chiefly determined by climatological factors
(Fig. 50). It can be seen from this that, even within a clearly
recognisable zoogeographical province, the vertical distribution of
a single group such as belemnites whose great stratigraphical value
is never doubted can give rise to totally misleading stratigraphical
conclusions. The vertical distribution and the interrelationship of
the different elements within such a group may be influenced by
factors quite different from chronological ones.

These two examples show that ecological and climatological-
geographical factors may sometimes inhibit the assumption that
similarity in fossil content implies similarity in time of formation
of the deposits in question. For this reason a biostratigraphical
correlation cannot automatically be regarded as a chronostratigraphical correlation without further research.

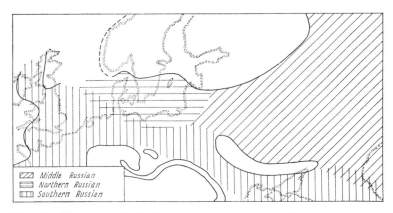

Fig. 50. Biogeographical subprovinces during the later Upper Cretaceous
in Central Europe.

Unfortunately there are no infallible criteria for distinguishing
immediately between those instances where a diagnosis of equal
age based on biostratigraphical correlations is justified and those
where it is not. Certain general considerations, however, may
enable a decision to be made. In the first place it is obvious that
the larger the number of elements of fauna and flora on which
conclusions concerning parity of age are based, the more reliable

these will be. The use of different groups exerts a certain control of reliability, as with the coral and brachiopod zones of the English Lower Carboniferous, where this method of control produced a negative result. In the second place the equation of biostratigraphical with chronostratigraphical correlations becomes more acceptable as the sensitivity to facies of the fossils in question decreases. Results based on groups with a great sensitivity to the facies or obtained in sequences of sediments that represent specialised environments should be regarded with caution.

The taxonomic level at which the biostratigraphical correlation is made also influences the evaluation of its relation to chronostratigraphy; the lower the taxonomic level the more probable the equation of biostratigraphy with chronostratigraphy. Correspondence at species level by no means excludes the possibility of a slight age difference, but if it is certain that examples of the same species are concerned, then the chronological difference cannot be too great. What is meant by " great " and " slight " in this context naturally depends on the range zone of the species in question. If the correlation is only based on correspondence in the genus, or on still higher taxonomic units, the chronological value decreases.

Finally it should be pointed out that correlations of whole sequences are much more valuable than incidental ones. If the entire faunal or floral sequence displays the same pattern in two areas, it must be concluded that the whole of the respective sequences were geologically formed, subdivision by subdivision, during the same interval of time. A correspondence of this sort can only be the result of a continual unhampered interchange of organisms between the two points concerned.

To sum up, it may be stated that, although the concept of contemporaneity remains a difficult point in geology, palaeontology forms the only generally usable basis for constructing a chronostratigraphical and therefore a chronological system. It should be remembered that the final stage, from biostratigraphy to chronostratigraphy, is full of pitfalls. A critical interpretation of all the available evidence, however, will see the investigator safely through this stage, and thus provide the essential background of a chronology, albeit a relative one, on which the evolution of the Earth's crust may be projected. The much quoted pronouncement of T. H. Huxley in 1862, that a Devonian fauna in England may be as old as a Silurian one in North America and a Carboniferous one in Africa may have indicated an acceptable possibility at the time. In the present knowledge of the evolution of life and of the migration of organisms this possibility can be excluded.

CHAPTER 5

SOME ASPECTS OF THE EVOLUTION OF LIFE

1. *Introduction*

It is clear from the previous chapter that there is a close correlation between the vertical succession of fossils and the development of life on the Earth. Without this organic evolution there would be no detailed chronological framework in which to place the Earth's history. Many other general aspects of palaeontology, however, are also closely connected with the continuous and progressive development of life. Without this development the close connection between the past distribution of organisms and the development of the geographical pattern of the Earth's crust would disappear. Organic evolution repeatedly provides a background to a discussion of the relationship between organisms and their environment, and in conclusion a number of points concerning this evolution must be submitted for closer examination.

The problems of " how " and " why " in organic evolution are so large that palaeontology can only make a modest contribution to their solution. In the study of the biological sciences, evolution is such a fundamental and central problem that it involves practically every branch of these sciences in one way or another. The discussion will here be limited to palaeontological aspects: the emphasis will lie on " how " rather than on " why ". Palaeontology is the science which can illuminate the historical element of the problem, in other words the relative time factor. It therefore does more than any other branch of the biological sciences to demonstrate the course of evolution as important through millions of years. The mechanism of evolution, however, evades the palaeontologist. He is, as it were, in the position of someone who stands at the edge of a busy motorway and sees the cars rush by in countless numbers, without ever learning how the petrol engine works.

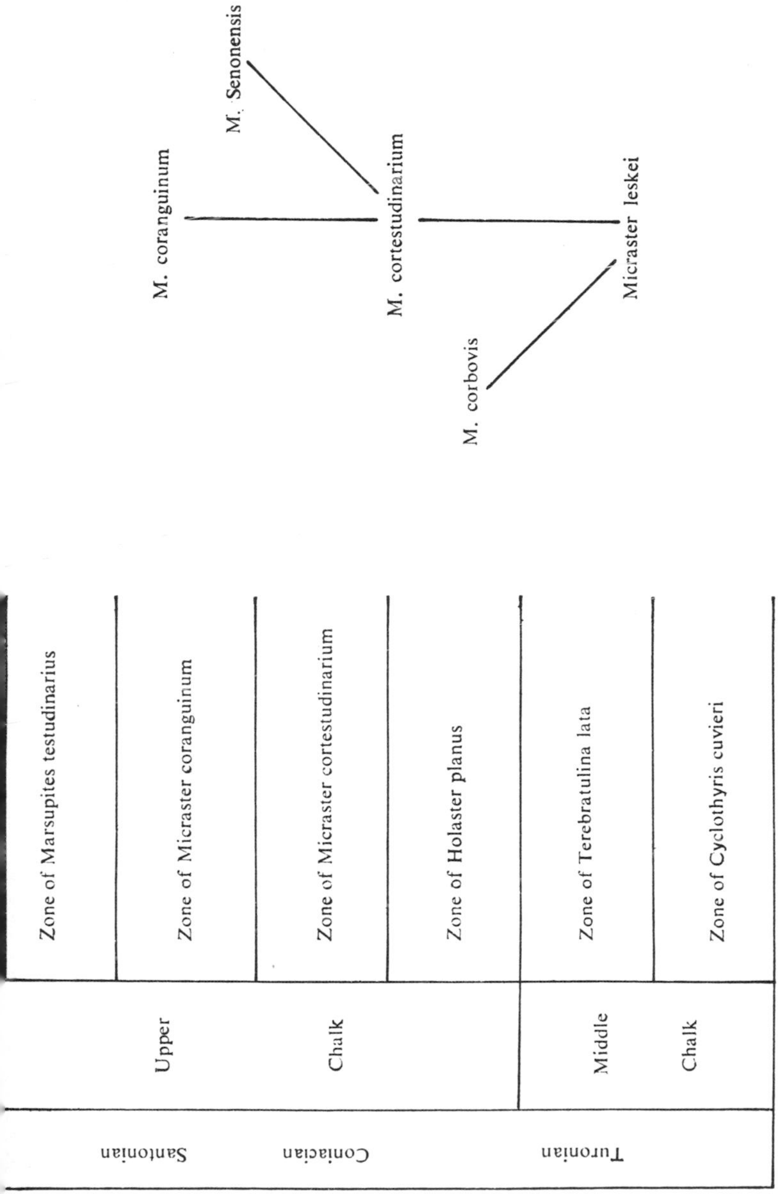

Fig. 51. Supposed relationship of *Micraster* species in British Middle and Upper Chalk.

2. From species to species

The smallest steps in evolution which the palaeontologist is able to observe are large in comparison with those which the geneticist studies, yet they form a welcome body of factual material at a level between the experimental information of the geneticist and the speculations of the palaeontologist about the evolution of the higher taxonomic units. For this reason it is disappointing that there are only a few detailed palaeontological studies of the changes which a species or genus undergoes from bed to bed in a single section. Naturally, not every fossil locality lends itself to such an examination. Such a section not only must show a full diversification within one species from bottom to top, but also contain a large number of specimens in each of the individual layers.

Perhaps one of the earliest recognised cases of evolution among the invertebrates is that of *Micraster* in the Middle Chalk and the lower part of the Upper Chalk of southern England. As early as 1899 Rowe showed that there existed a gradually and continuously evolving series of this echinoid from the Zone of *Cyclothyris cuvieri* upwards to the Zone of *Marsupites*. Although many forms have been given separate names in the course of the years, owing to the great variation shown by the many specimens present, it is now generally recognised that not more than five species are involved: *Micraster leskei* in the lowermost zone, leading to *M. cortestudinarium* and *M. corbovis* in the Zone of *Holaster planus,* where the latter becomes extinct, and two other species *M. coranguinum* and *M. senonensis* in the next higher zones (Fig. 51).

Among the changes observed in the course of the succeeding forms, the following features seem of particular interest :
- (*i*) the test became relatively broader; at the same time the broadest part as well as the tallest part of the test moved posteriorly;
- (*ii*) the anterior groove became deeper;
- (*iii*) the mouth moved anteriorly;
- (*iv*) the labrum became more pronounced; and
- (*v*) changes in the pore-pairs in the petaloid parts of the paired ambulacra.

Kermack (1954) showed that two side-lines can be recognised apart from the main line formed by *M. leskei, M. cortestudinarium* and

M. coranguinum. The first of the side branches originated in the Lata Zone and had already disappeared from the scene in the next higher Planus Zone. Its extreme forms distinguished as *M. corbovis* are markedly conservative in their features. Many intermediate forms, however, exist between this species and those of the main line. The second side-line originated in the Cortestudinarium Zone, in other words immediately after the extinction of *M. corbovis.* The specimens belonging to this line are distinguished as *M. (Isomicraster) senonensis.* Together with *M. coranguinum* it is a common species in the Coranguinum Zone. It disappeared in the next higher zone.

Kermack (1954) made an extensive statistical study of these two species. As a result of this work it appeared that in six of the seven characters applied, the ranges of variation of the two species overlap, the only distinct difference being the lack of a subanal fasciole in *M. senonensis.* Notwithstanding the many intermediate forms, probably representing a hybrid swarm, *M. coranguinum* and *M. senonensis* are considered to be good species by Kermack.

Later Nichols (1959) made a careful ecological analysis of the micrasters, starting from a study of some recent sea-urchins. As some morphological features of the test are clearly related with the function of the tube-feet, which in turn are related to the mode of life of the echinoids, a comparison of recent and fossil species with regard to morphology and mode of life seems justified.

The features of *M. leskei* suggest that it was only a shallow burrower. Some of the changes shown by the micrasters of the main line leading to *M. coranguinum* (such as changes in the peristomial region and in the position of the mouth, and in the degree of development of the labrum and depth of the anterior groove) point, by comparison with recent species, to a change in the mode of feeding. They relied more and more on ciliary currents, whereas the use of tube-feet became less important. This suggests that the micrasters of the main line became gradually adapted to deeper burrowing. As this change seems independent of environmental changes in the Chalk sea conditions, it appears that the micrasters gradually changed their ecological niche. The shallow-burrowing features are, however, retained by *M. corbovis.* It had already been shown by Kermack that this species is conservative in features when compared with the progressive changes in the

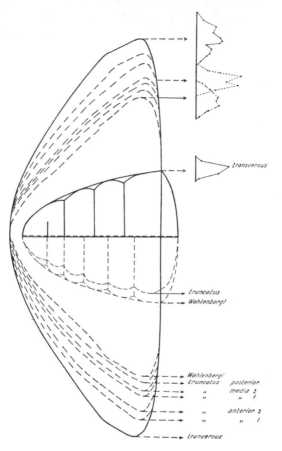

Fig. 52. The narrowing of the pygidium in the series *Olenus transversus - wahlenbergi,* measured in relation to the length. The curves (above right) give the range of variation in the measured specimens. After Kaufmann.

main *Micraster* line. *M. senonensis* probably represents a partial burrower which ploughed through the bottom rather than burrowing in it.

A somewhat different type of example is provided by the trilobites of the genus *Olenus* from the Upper Cambrian of Andrarum in southern Sweden (Kaufmann, 1933). The extensive and carefully collected material (approximately 1600 specimens from a vertical section 2·5 metres in height) belongs to six main species of *Olenus: gibbosus, transversus, truncatus, wahlenbergi, attenuatus* and *dentatus,* found in that order with *gibbosus* lowest in the section in which only the range zones of the latter two partly coincide. Four of these species, *gibbosus, transversus, attenuatus* and *dentatus,* can be assembled into a series without difficulty. The other two cannot be so

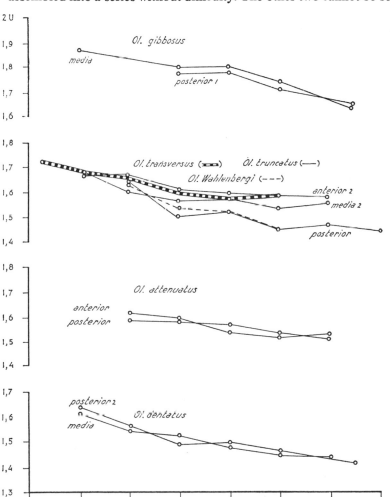

Fig. 53. Repetition of an ontogenetic phenomenon in phylogeny. The diagram shows the ratio length of the cephalon/width of the glabella (ordinate) related to the actual length of the cephalon (abscissa). From the individual curves it appears that the value of this ratio decreases in the ontogenetic evolution. From a comparison of the numerical value of the ratio length of cephalon/width of glabella in the different *Olenus* species it appears that the same phenomenon occurs in phylogeny. After Kaufmann.

11

arranged. According to Kaufmann, however, an extensive statistical study of the material shows that there is no direct genetic relationship between these species. They form a sequence but not one of direct descendants. The development of the species *transversus, truncatus* and *wahlenbergi,* however, took place in a manner that certainly suggests a direct relationship. The evolution of a single character, namely the narrowing of the pygidium, may serve to make this clear (Fig. 52).

Kaufmann made the interesting observation that certain characters change gradually, not only within the individual species, but also from species to species, while others remain constant within a species so that the change from one species to another is abrupt. Moreover the development of a number of gradually changing characters within the genus *Olenus* occurs in a similar way in the ontogeny. Here too a single example must suffice (Fig. 53).

A development comparable to that of the series *transversus, truncatus* and *wahlenbergi* also occurs within the species *gibbosus. attenuatus* and *dentatus* without leading to the creation of new species. Kaufmann distinguishes the early- and late-developing forms within the species mentioned which he designates as anterior, median and posterior.

Thus by detailed statistical research, collected trilobites can be arranged in four independent evolutionary series (Fig. 54). Only in one of the series does the development lead to the creation of new species, while in the other three series the differentiation remains below the species level. The way in which the development takes place within the species is, however, extraordinarily fascinating. If the four series have no direct inter-relationship with each other, it must be assumed that each is due to new immigrants. It is possible that this phenomenon is connected with a regression of the sea, the influence of which is perceptible throughout the whole Baltic region.

The evolution of the ceratites of the Germanic facies of the Middle Trias, investigated by Wenger (1957), provides an example of evolution independent of immigration. During the Trias the development of the ammonites was centred in the Tethys region and from there they penetrated twice into the Germanic basin in the Middle Trias. The first immigration took place during the Anisian (*Beneckeia,* etc.). This fauna died out with the closing off and

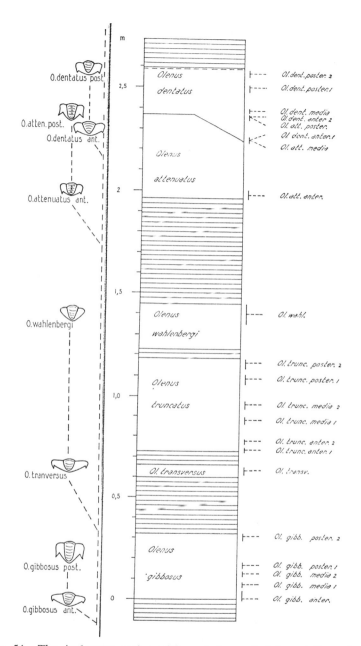

Fig. 54. The Andrarum section with a phylogenetic interpretation of the *Olenus* species encountered there given as four offshoots of an unknown main branch. The horizontally shaded parts produced no material. The short vertical lines to the right of the section indicate the parts of the section that provided abundant *Olenus* specimens, and from which approximately 1600 statistically processed specimens were taken. After Kaufmann.

155

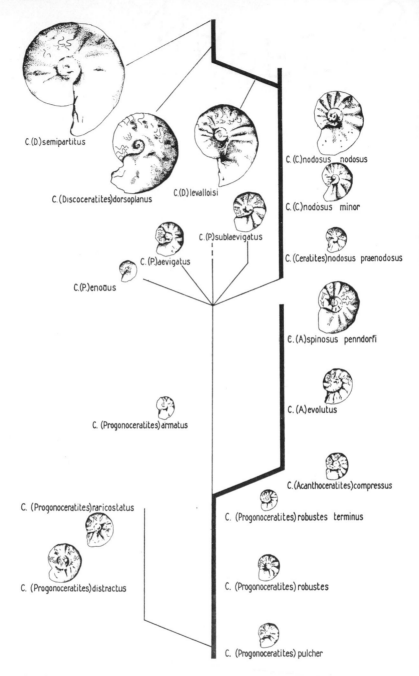

Fig. 55. Family tree of the genus *Ceratites* in the Germanic facies of the Middle Trias (after Wenger). The heavy line indicates the branches whose forms dominated the subsequent faunas. The specimens shown are 1/12 actual size.

156

subsequent evaporation of the Germanic basin which in the sedimentary succession is reflected in the "Anhydritgruppe". After the connection between the Tethys and the Muschelkalk Sea in the Germanic basin had been re-established in the Ladinian, a second ammonite invasion (Ceratite beds of the Upper Muschelkalk) followed. This ammonite fauna appears to have gone through a different development from that taking place in the Tethys.

Fig. 55 shows that the development began with comparatively small species of the subgenus *Progonoceratites*. Species with larger and more ornamented shells soon made their appearance, although the relations between the species in these lowest zones are not always clear. The transition to the *Acanthoceratites* is achieved via the relatively small *C. (Progonoceratites) robustus terminus*.

The subgenus *Acanthoceratites* then forms the most important element of the ammonite fauna. Successive species increased rapidly in size and then the whole branch suddenly disappeared with the extinction of the large *C. (Acanthoceratites) spinosus penndorfi*. Great variation in the subgenus *Progonoceratites* took place at almost the same time. This subgenus with few evolving forms had occupied only a modest place in the fauna while the acanthoceratites were predominant. The range of developing forms included both true ceratites and progonoceratite-like forms. It may therefore be assumed that the subgenus *Ceratites*, which after the acanthoceratites formed the most important and eventually the only ammonite group, cannot be derived from the acanthoceratites, as was formerly believed, but from the progonoceratites. In this branch of ceratitids increase in shell size can again be observed, a tendency that becomes still clearer in the last phases of the development with the subgenus *Discoceratites*. In the discoceratitids dichotomy again occurs, so that it is possible to speak of forms which no longer attain the typical nodus stage with long ribs, because of the premature termination of their physiological growth, or in other words of their ontogenetic development.

Of other investigations relating to the evolution of the ammonites, the detailed study made by Brinkmann (1929) of some of the ammonites belonging to the genus *Kosmoceras* from the Callovian of Peterborough must be mentioned here. Fig. 56 shows the phylogenetic arrangement of the material drawn up by Brinkmann after careful analysis. The five branches which co-existed

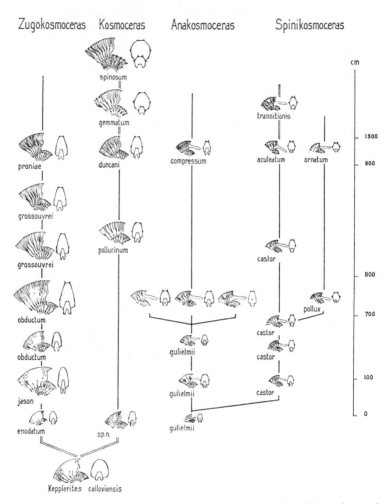

Fig. 56. Family tree of *Kosmoceras* from the Callovian of Peterborough. After Brinkmann. The fragments and cross-sections are shown in their actual size.

in the upper part of the examined section are classified into four subgenera and are good examples of a systematic grouping based on phylogenetic classification (Fig. 56). In the *Zugokosmoceras* series the shells generally increase in size. A similar trend is found in most of the other series, although it is less pronounced. In *Zugo-*

kosmoceras there is a striking change in the ornamentation of the shell. At first the living chamber is smooth, but later tubercles and finally ribs appear. The spacing of the latter becomes increasingly close, so much so that bundling of the outer ribs is caused. It is interesting to note that an intensified development of this feature is coupled with a temporary reduction in shell size. The same tendency towards larger shells is also found in the *Anakosmoceras* series where it goes with a progressive increase in the size of the lappets. The sculpturing of the shell undergoes only slight changes in this series.

The investigated material is also interesting because there is an obvious correlation between the various series in certain characters. The increase in shell size runs completely parallel in the *Zugokosmoceras* and *Anakosmoceras* series. The fewer specimens of *Kosmoceras* also give the impression of a parallel development. Only in *Spinikosmoceras* does the development differ in the higher part of the series. Parallel development can also be observed in the way in which the length of the lappets increases in *Anakosmoceras* and *Spinikosmoceras*. The bundling of the outer ribs, which occurs approximately simultaneously in all the series, except at a few points in the *Kosmoceras* and *Anakosmoceras series,* also exemplifies this parallelism. Although Fig. 56 shows some splitting of the series, the material examined does not display this very clearly. The splitting of the *Zugokosmoceras* and *Kosmoceras* series, of which the common ancestor *Kosmoceras (Kepplerites) calloviensis* is well known, took place just before the deposition of the strata which Brinkmann investigated. *Spinikosmoceras* appears after quite an important break in the sequence. It is clear, however, that this branch was initially characterised by a reduction in the number of ribs. *K. (Anakosmoceras) gulielmii* is one of those forms where bundling of the ribs occurs very early. In one of the two *Spinikosmoceras* branches the number of ribs increases again and this causes bundling at approximately the same time as in the other subgenera. Only in *S. ornatum* is bundling rare and so this species occupies a separate branch. The great variation in the number of ribs that occurs at one point in the *Anakosmoceras* branch could be ascribed to the splitting off of side branches, which soon disappeared from the scene.

3. *Evolution of higher categories*

The evolution of higher systematic units above the level of the species, and particularly above that of the genus, has a special attractiveness from a palaeontological point of view. The coming and going of major groups reveal more than anything else the fascinating phenomenon of evolution. The mighty development of the reptiles at the end of the Palaeozoic and in the Mesozoic, and their replacement by vertebrates of another type, the mammals, in the Cainozoic, speaks a more impressive language than, for example, the succession of various *Kosmoceras* species. In addition to this, the study of the evolution of major groups is the particular domain of the palaeontologist. Experimental research into evolution is necessarily conducted below the level of the species. Neontology is at present chiefly concerned with species, and groups of closely related species. On the other hand palaeontology, in which the element of time is taken into account, makes possible the study of the evolution of major groups of animals and plants over a long span of time. This change from lower to higher taxa is connected with a similar change in research techniques. It is not the experiment nor the extensive recent material that can be collected at will which forms the starting point, but scanty fossil material.

The terms micro-evolution and macro-evolution have often been used to express this difference. Simpson later added the term mega-evolution. The use of these terms has its dangers. It suggests that evolution takes place at only three different levels, whereas in fact there are as many levels of evolution as there are taxonomic categories. There is no specific reason for speaking of a different type of evolution above the level of the family. For some researchers the terms micro-evolution and macro-evolution indicate not only a difference in level, but also a difference in principle. For a long time the view has been fairly generally held that macro-evolution differs in principle from micro-evolution, and cannot be understood by applying the same factors that operate at species level. This distinction has perhaps meant less to palaeontologists, accustomed as they are to considering the great influence of the time factor. In the last few decades a change of viewpoint on this matter has also become noticeable among neontologists.

One of the most important points in this section must be to discover whether there is any reason for making a fundamental distinction between evolution within the species and from species to species on the one hand, and evolution in higher categories on the other.

Before going further into this question it is necessary to be quite clear about the artificial character of all higher categories. It is the size of a group more than anything else that determines its level in the systematic hierarchy. Numerous genera, as new species are added to them, are split up into subgenera and as a rule these subgenera soon achieve the status of genera. The group that was contained within the original genus then moves up to form a higher systematic unit. A striking example is provided by the ammonites which, not so very long ago, formed a single genus *Ammonites* and now forms an order with more than 1500 genera. This in no way detracts from the significance of the genus within the natural classification. Simpson said that if *Archaeopteryx* had remained the only flying vertebrate with feathers it would not have been considered as an early bird but as an exceptional reptile. On the other hand, if for example the flying reptiles (*Pterosauria*) had evolved further then it is unlikely that this new group, including the *pterosaurs,* would still be regarded as reptiles. Similarly it may be postulated that the family Equidae did not exist when only *Hyracotherium* trotted the Earth, although there can now be no doubt that it should be classified in this family.

From this can be deduced the important fact that higher categories do not need to have a primitive ancestral " prototype " possessing all the essential characteristics of the group. The question of whether *Archaeopteryx* is a bird or a reptile is unimportant. Both viewpoints can be defended with equal justification. *Archaeopteryx* is classified with the birds solely on the basis of its subsequent development.

Although higher categories have no prototype, transitional forms must have existed which connected new groups with older ones. It might be expected that these transitional forms should show in their characteristics on the one hand a relationship to the older group, and on the other have a tendency towards certain characteristics that reach full development in the new group. *Archaeopteryx* is an excellent example of such a link. Just as clearly as

Fig. 57. Sketch of the specimen of *Archaeopteryx lithographica* in Berlin. After de Beer. 1/3 actual size.

some of its characteristics, such as its teeth and the structure of its forelimbs, indicate the reptiles, others such as feathers point to the birds (Fig. 57).

One of the most surprising negative results of palaeontological research in the last century is that such transitional forms seem to be inordinately scarce. In Darwin's time this could perhaps be ascribed with some justification to the incompleteness of the palaeontological record and to lack of knowledge, but with the enormous number of fossil species which have been discovered since then, other causes must be found for the almost complete absence of transitional forms. Two factors, both of which have certainly been influential, may be considered responsible for the scarcity of such links at critical moments in the evolution of the higher units. If the evolution of these higher categories is studied against the background of physical time, it will be seen that at the critical period where transition to a new group takes place, the tempo of evolution is quicker. The earliest whales are known from the Middle Eocene. Even then these marine animals had the same general structure as all the later whales. It is true that since the Eocene the whale has undergone a definite evolution of which the lengthening of the cranium is one of the characteristic phenomena, but no major changes have been effected. Little is known for certain of the origin of the whales, but various features of the early forms from the Eocene suggest that they probably stemmed from a group of primitive predators, the Creodonta. Amongst other things the Eocene whales have differentiated teeth (Fig. 58), a feature which does not occur in later whales. Here too no transitional forms are known, but it is not difficult to imagine what numerous and far-reaching changes must have accompanied this transition from primitive land predator to fish-eating sea mammal. These changes are far more radical than anything in the later evolution of the whales. Nevertheless these major changes, such as the reduction of the neck, the pelvis and the hind limbs, and the development of the tail as a locomotive organ, took only a relatively short time, far less than the whole subsequent evolution of the group. If evolution had taken place at the same pace in the critical initial period as in later development, then whales would require to have had a Palaeozoic origin which is of course absurd. The Creodonta appeared in the early Palaeocene, so that the time needed for the evolution to the present whales lasted from the Palaeocene to the beginning of the Eocene—15 or 20 million years (as opposed to 50 million years for the subsequent evolution to the present whales). A phase of rapid evolution is a common phenomenon in most of the higher systematic units. It is apparent that evolution toward new groups generally took place comparatively rapidly and therefore in a relatively small number of generations.

This is one of the reasons why this interesting stage, which the palaeontologist would like to know about in as much detail as possible, is fairly poorly represented in fossil material. It is not the only reason, however, and perhaps not the most important one.

More theoretical investigations, in particular those of S. Wright, have made it clear that rapid evolution leading to new types has generally occurred in a limited geographical area, possibly within a population of relatively limited size. G. G. Simpson has made a number of studies of the palaeontological implications of Wright's work. A discussion of the views of these two men is beyond the scope of this book, particularly as fossils are hardly involved in their observations. What is most interesting at this stage is to see that an entirely non-palaeontological approach to the problem can explain why fossil material from critical phases of evolution, where the transition to new groups is effected, should be scarce. A new group does not arise as such; there is no primitive form already in possession of the essential characteristics of the whole group at an early stage. The development proceeds step by step—which is not necessarily incompatible with a rapid tempo—through forms which do show a trend towards a new group, but at the same time are still closely related to the parent group. At various moments in

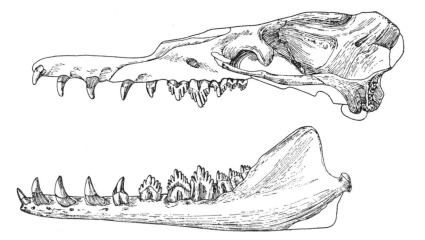

Fig. 58. Skull and lower jaw of *Basilosaurus*, an Eocene representative of the Archaeoceti. After Gregory.

the Mesozoic evolution of reptiles, for example, branches with mammalian tendencies can be observed. As long as such branches quickly disappear again, there can be no question of classifying the forms they contain as anything but reptiles. Only the later success of such a divergent group determines the inclusion of the transitional forms in the new group. It is usually difficult to follow an evolution of this type in detail for the reasons given above, and in addition to this a polyphyletic origin has been suggested more than once for the mammals.

There is, however, no reason to suppose that the factors active in the development of a new higher category are fundamentally different from those operative in the evolution of species, an evolution which the palaeontologist can sometimes show in his material (see Chapter 5, Section 2) or the geneticist demonstrate experimentally. It is always " the stream of heredity that makes phylogeny " (Simpson 1945, p. 5).

It appears that the most important factor determining development towards new higher categories is the opening up of new ecological niches. In general, such a new group will end up in a higher place in the systematic hierarchy, as the range of ecological niches becomes wider. The latter leads to some measure of differentiation within the group as a whole, and to a large extent determines its systematic evaluation.

Expressed in anatomical and morphological terms the evolution of a new higher category means therefore the development of a new character or characters which either opens the way to a new environment or gives the group an advantage over others in the same environment. Initially such a new character does not of course arise in a group but in a single evolving branch. The species which belong to this branch usually show a combination of old and new characters which makes the drawing of systematic boundaries difficult and would make it much more difficult if material from these critical stages was more abundant. The first appearance of an essentially new character ought to provide a systematic criterion. This is, however, only useful if the new character is consolidated by a successful development in a larger group. The repeated attempts towards a mammalian development during the Mesozoic history of the reptiles are a good example of this.

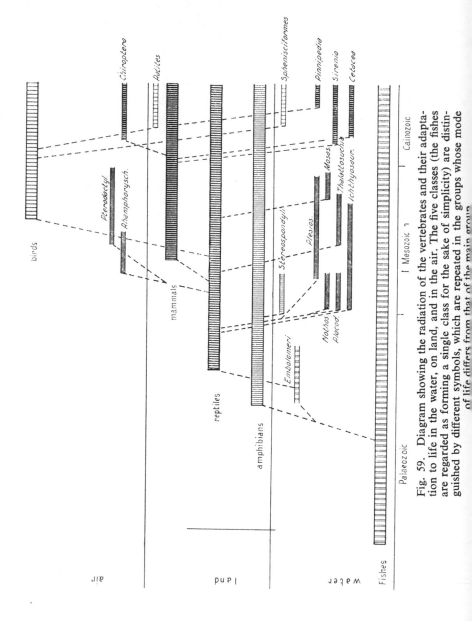

Fig. 59. Diagram showing the radiation of the vertebrates and their adaptation to life in the water, on land, and in the air. The five classes (the fishes are regarded as forming a single class for the sake of simplicity) are distinguished by different symbols, which are repeated in the groups whose mode of life differs from that of the main group.

Within the subphylum of the vertebrates the evolution of new classes represents adaptation to a new environment on the one hand, and on the other represents improved adaptation to environments already populated by other vertebrates (Fig. 59).

The oldest vertebrates, the fish, which in themselves form a rather heterogeneous group and are nowadays divided into four separate classes, had in common the fact that they were all water inhabiting. In the light of this the evolution during the Upper Devonian of the amphibians from the spiny-finned fish (Crossopterygii) can be seen as an attempt by these vertebrates to colonise an ecological habitat hitherto virtually unoccupied by animals. This meant a radical change in the vertebrates' mode of life which was associated with various major alterations in their structure to accommodate new methods of respiration and locomotion. As is so often the case, the same trend occurs more than once in the development of a particular group. In the Dipnoi (lungfish) one of the structural changes essential to the transition to life on land was effected as early as the Middle Devonian, but without producing further development in this direction. It is true that some recent lungfish can survive times of drought buried in the beds of completely dried up rivers, but it is not possible to term this a conquest of the land. In this respect the development which led via the Crossopterygii to the primitive amphibians represents a more successful attempt, but even here adaptation to terrestrial life is not complete. Although locomotion and respiration have become reasonably well adjusted to the new environment, this has not been the case with propagation; and for this part of their life cycle, the amphibians remain dependent on water.

The amphibians represent a vertebrate group which made the first attempt to go over to a terrestrial mode of life, and to a certain extent succeeded. The reptiles and mammals are two groups of vertebrates that have attained a greater degree of adaptation to life on land. The two groups have successively displayed an enormous diversification, whereby within their general structural and environmental limits they evolved in many different directions to inhabit various ecological niches. The success of these two groups is due largely to a further modification in the means of reproduction which became quite independent of the water—eggs with shells were developed by the reptiles, and the mammals became viviparous. In addition to this the structure of the organs of locomotion improved, particularly in the mammals.

After the initial aquatic stage of the fish, the whole evolution of the vertebrates, including the birds, provides an instructive example of the evolution of new classes under the influence of adaptation to a new environment, as in the amphibians and the birds, or of improved adaptation to such an environment, as in the reptiles and mammals. The fact that, in each of these groups, trends still occur which deviate from the general course of evolution of the group as a whole in no way detracts from the value of this example. On the contrary, such trends can be regarded as constituting an analogous development on a lower taxonomic level. Just as birds form a separate class within the vertebrate subphylum, so bats form a separate order within the mammalian class.

Divergent evolutionary trends of this sort occur in the reptiles as well as in birds and mammals. Among the reptiles there are on the one hand certain groups which developed limited powers of flight, while on the other hand various groups returned to the water. Because of the retention of the essential features of reptilian structure, the problems overcome in the initial evolution of the reptiles occurred again in reverse. In some marine reptiles, such as the Plesiosauria, the limbs underwent only a few changes, in others fins reappeared, this time with a modified reptilian skeleton as a basis, and the function of propulsion was transferred to the tail, as in the Ichthyosauria. Reproduction sometimes underwent radical modifications. The Ichthyosauria are usually regarded as viviparous, but other groups retained the original reptilian egg. The astonishing result is that marine turtles have a life cycle exactly opposite to that of the amphibians. The sea turtles have to return to land for the propagation of their kind. In some respects the evolution of the mammals is strikingly similar to that of the reptiles. Here too there is one group, the bats, that has developed the power of flight, and there are other groups that have become re-adapted to an aquatic mode of life; the ways in which this latter adaptation has been achieved vary, particularly with regard to the means of propulsion.

Secondary adaptation to life on land or water occurs among birds, showing how in a few branches the trend that has determined the evolution of the group as a whole may be abandoned. In the birds this implies a loss of ability to fly. Some birds, such as the ostriches, are now purely ground dwellers, others, like the penguins, have become adapted to an aquatic life.

It would be interesting at this stage to subject the invertebrates to a closer examination from this viewpoint. Unfortunately this is not possible to anything like the same extent as for the vertebrates. Firstly, part of the differentiation of the invertebrates took place in Precambrian times, for which palaeontological evidence is sparse. Knowledge of the early Palaeozoic is also rather limited because of the absence of continental deposits. A more complete picture of the evolution of the invertebrates does not emerge until the Devonian. Secondly, the structure of the hard parts of the invertebrates is not so closely related with function and mode of life as in the vertebrates. There is only one invertebrate phylum that includes aquatic, terrestrial and flying forms, namely the Arthropoda. Lastly, invertebrate palaeontologists generally show less interest in evolution than vertebrate palaeontologists. Nevertheless, there are analogous examples among the invertebrates of diversification influenced by ecological adaptation. Thus the replacement of the brachiopods by the molluscs, especially the lamellibranchs, is reminiscent of the replacement of the amphibians by the reptiles and of the reptiles by the mammals. Within the molluscs the development of the cephalopods may be regarded as an adaptation to a new mode of life. There is no reason to suppose that the evolution of the invertebrates should have differed in principle in the way in which it was effected from that of the better known vertebrates.

It may be concluded that higher categories did not originate as such; that there was therefore no primitive, archaic type in which all the essential characteristics of the group were already united; and that the evolution which produced higher categories and evolution from species to species were governed in principle by the same laws. Finally, the great evolutionary bursts that give rise to a major group appear to have taken place mainly under the influence of ecological adaptation.

4. *The tempo of evolution*

The speed of evolution has already been referred to briefly in the previous section. There, without going into detail, it was established that the speed with which evolution takes place in a particular group is not always constant. The question that immediately arises is how the speed of evolution can be measured, that is to say, how the amount of change can be expressed in relation to a time scale. Radiometric time is preferable as a scale of measurement, but the small number of points on the relative time scale for which the approximate age in years has been determined has to suffice. These points are usually widely spaced, so that for short intervals of time which fall between them no more than a rough approximation can be obtained.

Further difficulties are raised by the problems of how to express the amount of change quantitatively. As long as attention can be focused on a single, easily measurable character, such as the changes in the dimensions of a shell or a skeletal element, no special difficulties arise. Sometimes it can be an advantage not to measure a single character but to make use of the relationship or proportion of two characters. It has, however, already been demonstrated that a whole complex of characters undergoes change and that within such a complex conflicting trends can occur. In the evolution of most lineages within the genus *Kosmoceras* the increase in the dimensions of the shell and the modification in the pattern of the ribs are characteristic features. Exactly at the times when important changes take place in the ribs, the trend towards larger shells seems to be interrupted. Size, if taken by itself, would give an incomplete picture of the evolution of this genus.

When in an evolutionary series the change is of a compound nature, it is generally not possible to express quantitatively the whole pattern of the morphological change in a satisfactory way. It is this pattern which usually forms the basis of the species in palaeontology. It is possible to adopt a different approach, and discover the tempo at which one species is replaced by its successor in a phylogenetic series. It seems that the speed of evolution within a certain lineage can be approached along two different lines: (*i*) morphologically, based on a single changing character or number of characters and (*ii*) taxonomically, based on all the characters as

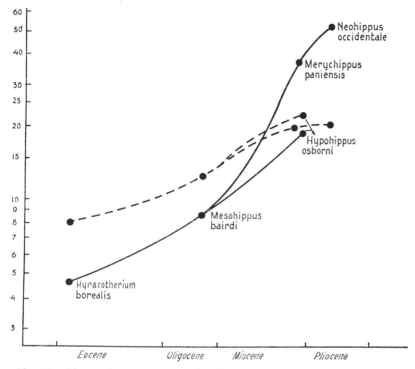

Fig. 60. Linear change (average values in mm on the logarithmic ordinate) of two measurements of the third molar of five Equidae. Black dots give the average values of the height of the paraconus (continuous line) and the width of the ectolophe (broken line); the connecting lines indicate the phylogenetic relationships between the species; the four dots on the broken line and its lower branch relate to the same species as those on the continuous line and its upper branch, successively therefore *Hyracotherium, Mesohippus, Merychippus* and *Neohippus*. From the position of the points it appears that (*i*) the two measurements represented here increase in the course of evolution but not to the same degree, and (*ii*) that a separation occurs in the evolution whereby the height of the paraconus increases more quickly and the length of the ectolophe increases more slowly in the branch leading to *Neohippus* than in that leading to *Hypohippus*. After Simpson.

expressed in the distinction between species and higher categories. The latter has the advantage that the whole complex of characters which change is taken into consideration, but has the disadvantage that to some extent a subjective element—the definition and distinction of successive species—is introduced.

The ideal way of measuring amounts of change would naturally be to utilise genetic change for this purpose. Even with recent material, this is an extremely difficult problem, it has only been done for a few *Drosophilia* populations, and with fossil material it is impossible to apply. The amount of morphological change (change in the phenotype) can usually be taken as an approximate

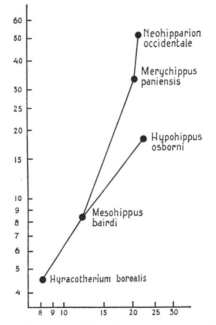

Fig. 61. The same data as in Fig. 60, but instead of being represented independently on a time axis, they are now given in relation to each other, with the height of the paraconus as the ordinate and the length of the ectolophe as the abscissa (both with logarithmic scale). The relationship shown expresses the degree of hypsodonty which increases in both branches, but not by the same amount.

indication of the change in the genotype, so that the palaeontological approach to the problem need not be too unsatisfactory.

The simplest way to measure the amount of morphological change is to trace out the linear measurements of a certain property. Fig. 60 gives an example of this. Instead of a single linear change, the modification in the relationship between two linear measurements can sometimes give useful results. This holds good, for example, for tracing changes of forms in shells, but the change in other inter-related characters may be profitably approached in this way. In Fig. 61 this has been done for the data contained in Fig. 60.

Naturally this method is not capable of illuminating more than a limited aspect of evolution. Even if the character or combination of characters under investigation is correctly selected the picture of evolution remains one-sided. If a greater number of characters are considered at the same time, then the chances of achieving a simple objective expression of this in a numerical scale diminish greatly. The most satisfactory method is then to evaluate the various characters of the successive members of an evolutionary series in figures, in relation to the starting and finishing points of this development, and to calculate an average for each member which gives its relative place in the series. Olson has done this with various mammal-like reptiles by estimating in figures their morphological approach to true mammalian characteristics. Westoll did something similar with the evolution of lungfish. He evaluated in figures the amount of change per million years. The upper graph of Fig. 62 shows his results. The lower graph of the same figure is based on the general evaluation of the relative place of each member of the evolutionary series of the lungfish in relation to the starting and finishing points, the most primitive forms being assigned 0 and the recent lungfish 100. It is obvious that the two graphs express the same thing in different ways. The first part of the upper curve, with a rapidly increasing evolutionary level, corresponds with the steep part of the second curve, and so on. This method requires a profound knowledge of the group concerned, and even then a certain subjectivity cannot be excluded. It should be borne in mind, therefore, that a large part of systematic palaeontology, and of the distinction and definition of species, is founded more on subjective than on objective evaluations of characters.

Both of Westoll's graphs illustrate clearly the great differences in the tempo of evolution within a single group. During the first million years in the history of lungfish their development was relatively swift so that at the end of the Devonian they had, morphologically speaking, progressed a long way towards their modern form. In the two hundred and fifty million years of their further development the changes were much smaller.

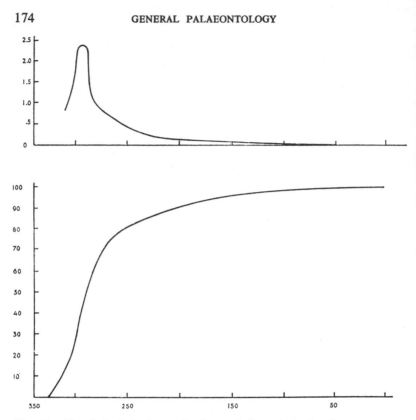

Fig. 62. Morphological change in the evolution of the lungfish: *below*: evaluated in ciphers from 0 to 100 (ordinate), placed on a time axis (in millions of years); *above*: the same data as in the lower graph, but given as an expression of the rate of change per million years, placed on the same time axis. After Westoll and Simpson.

At this stage the second method of measuring the speed of evolution, the taxonomic, must be considered. Although the curves of Fig. 62 are based on morphological not taxonomic data, it is evident that as a consequence of the large number of characters used by Westoll (more than 20) there is no great difference here between the morphological and the taxonomic methods of approach to the problem. It is obvious that in the time interval of the lower curve of Fig. 60 the species succeed each other much more rapidly there than afterwards. In fact the distinction of species is also dependent on the subjective evaluation of a great number of characteristics.

In measuring the speed of evolution along taxonomic lines the same objections apply as in the morphological method with its use of a large number of characters. These objections become most apparent when a comparison of different higher systematic units is attempted. Genera are usually more satisfactory than species for these purposes, but then the objection remains that it is difficult to determine how far genera in mammals are comparable with genera in molluscs or foraminifers. Nevertheless measurement of evolutionary tempo along taxonomic lines opens up a number of interesting perspectives. This particularly applies to the length of life of taxonomic units—species and genera, etc. A good example of the enormous differences which exist in this respect is obtained by looking at the contemporary flora and fauna, and discovering when their elements originated. In addition to numerous species which appear in the Upper Cainozoic, many of which did not emerge until the Pleistocene, there is for example the freshwater crustacean *Triops cancriformis* which first occurs in the Middle Keuper. With its 180 million years this probably holds the record among species. The differences are even more marked with genera. Alongside numerous genera which appeared in the Pleistocene there is the brachiopod genus *Lingula* which first appeared in the Ordovician.

Another method of learning about the tempo of evolution in the taxonomical aspect is the comparison of faunas whose date of isolation is known. Thus among the South American mammals which migrated from North America roughly during the transition from the Pliocene to the Pleistocene, there is now no single species which is identical to a North American species. Some South American species have already been placed in new genera. Beirne divides the present mammalian fauna of the British Isles into three groups, according to the date of their immigration. Of the first group, which immigrated between 50,000 and 100,000 years ago, 57 per cent differs at species level from the continental fauna. In the second group, which has inhabited these islands for about 25,000 years, the percentage is nil, but 91 per cent of the group can be classified as belonging to different subspecies. In the third group, consisting of post-glacial immigrants, there is no difference between continental and insular fauna even at subspecific level.

Figures such as these provide information about the time needed by new species or new genera to evolve, but they say nothing about the life-duration of the species or other units. Data for this must be taken exclusively from extinct units. Simpson has done this with the series of horse-like creatures which led to the recent *Equus*. According to modern views this series consists of eight genera (apart from *Equus* itself). The age of the first genus *Hyracotherium* can be estimated at about 60 million years, which therefore gives an average life-duration of 7·5 million years per genus, or 0·13 genus per million years. Comparable figures have been found for other series of mammals. It is usually assumed that the evolution of mammals is characterised by a high tempo. As an example from an entirely different group Simpson quotes the Palaeozoic and Triassic ammonoids for which he calculates an average life-duration of 20 million years per genus. Taking into consideration that this group provides a large number of good stratigraphic index fossils, the figure seems very high. Schindewolf arrives at a life-duration per genus of 1 to 3 million years in stratigraphically important genera from the same group, and believes that the relatively low number of genera that persisted over a very long time-span cannot greatly influence the average of the whole group.

Zeuner believed that differences exist between marine and terrestrial animals with regard to the speed of evolution. The more stable conditions under which marine creatures live result in a lower tempo. On the basis of the research he conducted, mainly into mammals and insects, he considered a life-duration of ½ million years per species to be the minimum for land animals.

An examination of the tempo of evolution in which more attention is devoted to the " horizontal " element has the advantage that the question of phylogenetic relationship within a group need not be taken into account. This being so, it is possible to take another look at the invertebrates. Here there are some disadvantages: (*i*) lack of palaeontological knowledge and incompleteness of the palaeontological record, (*ii*) discrepancies in the amount of information about slow-developing and fast-developing groups (the latter are usually less well known), (*iii*) differences in the amount of information available about various faunas, due to differences in the monographic activity of systematic palaeontologists. How far these disadvantages cancel each other out is difficult to say; they have opposite effects on the resultant data.

One method of processing the data is to calculate the average life-duration of all the genera in a higher category. Some data of this sort, illustrating the great difference between various groups, are given in the table below. Such figures only represent averages. Within the development of one group there are great differences, e.g. the Devonian genera of lungfish have an average life-duration

TABLE

Average life-duration of genera (in millions of years)

Ammonites	*c* 3 (Schindewolf)
Land carnivores	8 (Simpson)
Lungfish	30 (Westoll)
Palaeozoic ostracods	37 (Cooper)
Brachiopods	40 (Schuchert and Le Vene)
Foraminifers	71 (Schindewolf)
Prosobranchiate gastropods	73 (Schindewolf)
Lamellibranchs	78 (Simpson)

of only 7 million years, but the Mesozoic genera have one of 115 million years, a difference that entirely corresponds with what is shown in Fig. 62. Such an analysis of the averages for various phases from the development of a group gives a much clearer idea of evolutionary tempo. But the differences between various groups still give cause for speculation about whether the speed of evolution is in fact different in various groups or whether it is the evaluation of genera in these groups that varies.

The average figures in the table give no indication as to the amount of spread of the individual life-duration figures. An average of 40 can equally well be the result of the numbers between 35 and 45 as of numbers between 10 and 70 (and, of course, of numbers between 10 and 45 if the high numbers have a high frequency). An impression of the spread is gained by constructing a frequency curve of the life-duration of the genera in a group. Fig. 63 gives a few such curves in which a distinction is made between the life-durations of extinct genera and those of living

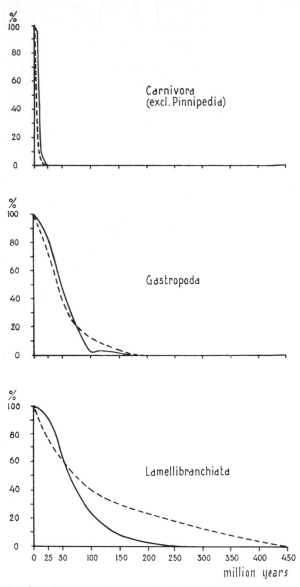

Fig. 63. Survivorship curves for recent and extinct genera of lamellibranchs, gastropods and land carnivores. The curves are summation curves, so that each point of a curve indicates the percentage of genera which possesses a minimum longevity given by the corresponding point on the abscissa. For extinct genera (continuous line) the curves thus give the longevity as established by fossils. The curves of recent genera (broken line) show longevity based on fossil representatives. Compiled from data by Simpson and Schindewolf.

178

genera. It can be expected that the second curve, containing the genera whose history is not yet completed, will follow the first one closely and with a bias towards the lower figures. In carnivores this is in fact the case, but in gastropods and lamellibranchs it is only partly so. This is probably a result of the number of recent genera with a very long history. There have been similar genera at earlier stages, but because their later history has generally been characterised by a small number of individuals, they have been more likely to escape the notice of palaeontologists than neontologists.

It should be borne in mind that the groups compared in Fig. 63 differ greatly in one historical aspect. Although all three groups survive in the recent fauna, the history of carnivores goes back to the Palaeocene, while that of the gastropods and lamellibranchs goes back to the Cambrian and the Ordovician respectively. In groups with such a long history, phases of rapid and of slow evolution occur. On the other hand such groups as the carnivores and nearly all other mammalian groups whose first appearance is of relatively recent date mainly show a rapid evolution and have not yet entered a stage characterised by more stabilised evolutionary conditions. This difference is no doubt largely responsible for the differences shown in the groups which are represented in Fig. 63. Williams (1957) has pointed out that the average duration for brachiopod genera during the entire history of the brachiopods is 53 million years, but the average duration for Ordovician genera is only 16 million years. Similar differences occur in the history of the lungfish as referred to earlier in this section.

So far the argument has been exclusively concerned with the tempo of evolution in a single developmental series. For whether the problem is approached morphologically or taxonomically it is always the tempo at which morphological changes, or new species, genera, etc., occur one after another in sequence that is measured. This is what could be called evolution in a vertical sense. There is, however, an entirely different way of tackling the problem of the tempo of evolution, namely to observe carefully the number of species, genera or higher categories that exist simultaneously. It has long been known that in this respect too there are great differences both between various stages of the development of a single group and between different groups. When it is said that the

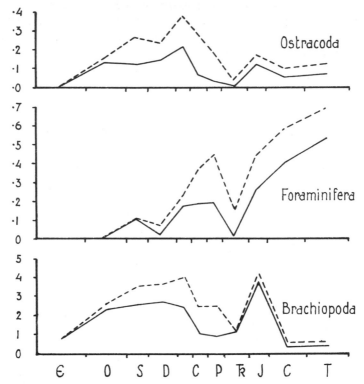

Fig. 64. Total number of genera (broken line) per million years, and number of new genera (continuous line) per million years for three groups of invertebrates. After Newell. In these and some of the following figures the Carboniferous is sometimes represented by two separate points for Lower and Upper Carboniferous (Mississippian and Pennsylvanian), as the published data were not always sufficient to calculate one new number. Some graphs show a striking difference between the Lower and Upper Carboniferous, from which it appears that the choice of the chronological units on the time axis can have considerable influence on the resulting picture.

graptolites reached their peak in the Ordovician it is not morphological or taxonomic rates of evolution that are implied, but rather the generally known phenomenon that in the Ordovician a large number of new species and genera appeared, and that numerous species and genera existed contemporaneously irrespective of their phylogenetic relationships. Most of the large groups have had one or more such periods in the course of their existence, but only in recent times has this interesting facet been studied in a more systematic manner. Because of their more objective and stable character genera or higher categories seem more useful units in this respect than species, which in palaeontology always suffer from a large dose of subjectivity.

The horizontal aspect is most clearly represented in taxonomic frequency curves which express absolute numbers of species, both more often of genera or higher categories on a time axis. The smaller the units in which time is expressed on the time axis, the more detailed and reliable is the picture gained. As a rule, however, rather large time units have to be used. In order to compensate to some extent for the effect of the unequal length of these units, it is sometimes advisable to give on the other axis the average number of taxonomic units per million years (Fig. 64), or to replace the curve with a histogram.

The total number of taxonomic units at a particular moment, or in a particular interval of time, is the result of the number of new units that have emerged and the number that have disappeared, either through becoming extinct or by evolving into new units. From the viewpoint of evolutionary tempo, both numbers are very instructive as it is these that determine the trend of the curve for absolute numbers.

A rising curve means that the number of new appearances exceeds that of the units that disappear; the steeper the curve, the greater the amount by which the former exceed the latter. Taxonomically speaking, the group then broadens out.

When looking at evolutionary phenomena in this way the investigator is exposed to a number of the hazards referred to earlier in this section. The number of species or genera in a family or in an order depends on certain random factors. The activity of a systematic palaeontologist, studying a particular group of a certain age, may appreciably affect the results obtained by plotting absolute numbers of species or genera, and even more so if the relation between existing and newly appearing species or genera for a certain period is taken into account. Williams (1957) has argued convincingly that even the activity of a single palaeontologist may have a noticeable effect on the position of peaks in a graph representing absolute numbers of brachiopod genera in successive periods. If this holds true for brachiopods the same effect may be

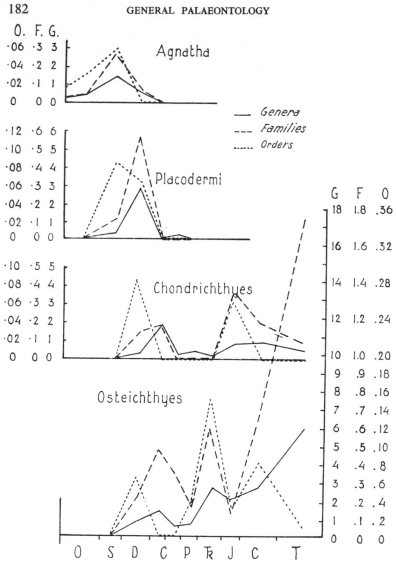

Fig. 65. Number of new genera, new families and new orders for the four classes of fish. After Simpson.

expected in other groups. The number of genera or species is not only affected by the discovery of new ones, but also by taxonomic splitting of already established groups. On the other hand it can be expected that the influence of the activity of individual palaeontologists upon the total number of genera or species of a certain period decreases as palaeontological knowledge increases and the gradually increasing number of active palaeontologists naturally leads to a more balanced growth of total numbers of genera or species. Notwithstanding these restrictions a closer study of some results obtained along these lines seems worthwhile.

As far as the study of evolutionary phenomena is concerned, the rate at which new genera or higher taxonomic units appear is particularly illuminating. Fig. 65 gives the number of new genera, families and orders per million years for the Palaeozoic and Mesozoic periods and the Cainozoic in the four classes of fishes. Firstly it appears that some curves have a single peak, others have more than one. The latter is usually the result of the development of new genera within the unit. Thus the sharp rise in the number of genera in the Osteichthyes (bony fish) during and after the Cretaceous is caused by the development of the superorder Teleostei. The maxima preceding this are the result of the flourishing of other superorders. Secondly, the maxima for the various categories sometimes appear to coincide, as in the Agnatha, but at other times they clearly occur in succession.

Usually the maxima of higher categories precede those of lower ones. This means that initially a relatively small number of new genera represents a large number of new orders, and that not until a succeeding stage do these orders fill out with the appearance of numerous new families and genera. The curves show obvious examples of this at various points; the phenomenon is particularly well marked in the Placodermi curves. The same phenomenon appears in the invertebrates. Fig. 66 gives some examples of this.

Phases in which the rate of appearance of new species, genera, etc. is speeded up, producing a strongly marked lateral differentiation, is a normal phenomenon in the history of higher categories. The terms " explosive evolution " or " bursts " are used to describe such phases which coincide with phases of rapid morphological and/or taxonomic evolution, and therefore with a rapid succession of species and genera in a simple evolutionary series. The opposite of explosive evolution is represented by a slow rate of morphological and taxonomic evolution, and the absence of this lateral

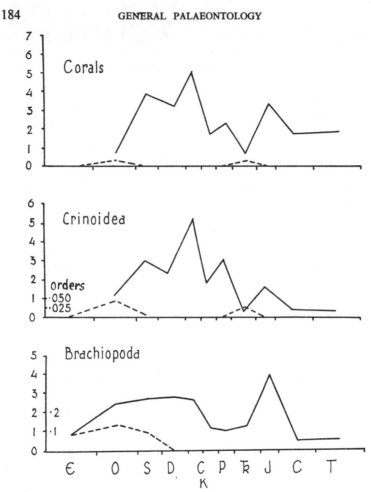

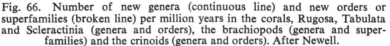

Fig. 66. Number of new genera (continuous line) and new orders or superfamilies (broken line) per million years in the corals, Rugosa, Tabulata and Scleractinia (genera and orders), the brachiopods (genera and super-families) and the crinoids (genera and orders). After Newell.

differentiation. This is the characteristic pattern shown in the evolution of " living fossils ".

5. Directional trends

Evolution implies change. The rate at which this change takes place has been examined in the previous section, and now the

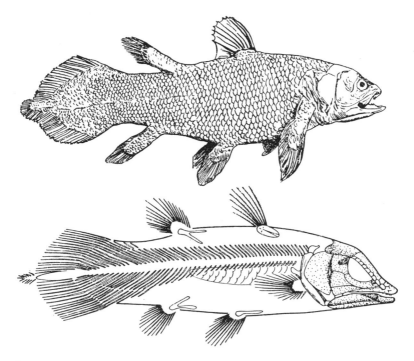

Fig. 67. *Latimeria* (above) and *Macropoma,* two representatives of the Coelacanthini, a recent and a Cretaceous specimen respectively. After Gregory.

direction in which it tends must be studied. The term directional trend seems innocent enough, but there is probably no subject in the whole field of evolutionary study about which so much has been written and so many conflicting opinions expressed. This is not surprising for the subject represents one of the most fundamental problems not only of evolution but also of many other areas of study. The question whether the course of evolution through millions of years has been determined by a guiding principle (autogenesis, finalism), is beyond the scope of palaeontology. The aim of this section will be more modest; it will only attempt to examine the directions of evolutionary trends in certain series. The term direction is here used in its most neutral sense, and without any philosophical implications. If it is recognised that evolution implies change, which is ultimately a form of movement, it follows that change must always take place in a certain direction: that direction can alter from moment to moment, however, so that over a period of time change may appear to be directionless.

It is apparent from the examples which have been discussed in this chapter that a lineage is usually dominated by a definite trend for a certain period of time. Such a trend may be expressed in several different characters simultaneously. Before the 1940s, when the gap which had separated the study of evolution from genetics began to be narrowed, the importance of linear evolution was perhaps overestimated. Many evolutionary lineages, on closer examination of more extensive material, appear to be less recti-linear than had previously been thought. They exhibit a general tendency in a particular direction, but not without interruptions or divergences. This has been demonstrated a number of times in the earlier part of the chapter—on a small scale in the evolution of the genus *Kosmoceras*, and on a large scale in the emergence of aquatic forms in the reptiles or the mammals which could be regarded as a clear divergence from orthogenesis. This does not alter the fact that the evolution of the aquatic forms may itself show a measure of rectilinearity for a considerable time.

As far as can be deduced from the usually scanty material of the palaeontologist, linear evolution does occur, but it is difficult to show that the evolution of higher taxonomic units progresses along such lines. This is not the case even in many smaller units. A better statement of the position would be that many linear developments become fragmented, each of the fragments being linear in itself, but not a straight continuation of the preceding development. The general development may even proceed for a considerable time in a completely opposite direction.

One of the commoner tendencies of this type is an increase in the dimensions of the organisms of a group. If this process con-tinues indefinitely, gigantism results. This phenomenon is often regarded as a characteristic of moribund groups that are shortly to become extinct. Gigantism is a relative concept, however, and many examples can be quoted where it is not followed by the extinction of the group concerned, but by a reduction in dimen-sions and the continued existence of the group. Various recent researchers have indicated cases in which positive and negative trends in the dimensions of animals can be viewed as normal phenomena of ecological adaptation, especially to climatic conditions. Various species of mammals which are widely distributed in cold areas are known to be larger than the same species in warmer regions, a phenomenon that may be connected with the fact that, in a purely thermodynamic sense, large animals are rather more efficient than small ones. The increase in the dimensions of many mammals in the Pleistocene and their recent reduction are no more than an adaptive reaction to climate.

In speculating about the evolutionary trends as shown by palaeontological material, distinction should be made between the more obvious and the more significant features. Every group known by fossils shows differently orientated branches in the course of its history. Fossil evidence lends no support to the idea that there was a predetermined or built-in goal towards which development took place. On the contrary it seems that fossil evidence is quite consistent with the view that the evolutionary changes took place because of natural selection of the genotypes which were most suited to exploit certain environmental opportunities. Selection may operate, generally speaking, in the same direction for some time. This is what Simpson has called orthoselection. It may well be responsible for many of the apparent linear trends observed among fossils. Orthoselection lasts only as long as the environmental opportunity which favours it.

Similar linear trends can often be observed in two or more closely placed evolutionary series. Such lineages have, therefore, a common ancestral form. The term parallel evolution is used if, after an initially divergent phase, the separate branches do not move further apart. This phenomenon occurs in many groups. The various evolving lineages which Brinkmann distinguished in the genus *Kosmoceras* form a particularly good example. If the divergence between branches is slight, parallel evolution is often difficult to recognise and very misleading for the systematist. It has been seen that the improved systematics which Brinkmann introduced for this genus are based on a detailed analysis of phylogeny. There is reason to suppose that in many of the less thoroughly studied groups, numerous genera, and perhaps higher categories, should not be regarded as natural phylogenetic units as they include forms which are actually from various lineages.

The matter becomes even more difficult when different branches evolve towards each other. Buckman introduced the term homeo-morphy to describe this phenomenon. This term has not had exactly the same significance for all later researchers. Cloud (1948) attempted a taxonomic definition of the concept whereby corres-pondence should concern the whole organism and not only certain structures. A logical consequence of this is that the term homeo-morphy is used only when there is danger of taxonomic confusion. Superficially an ichthyosaur may bear a great resemblance to a whale in a number of ways, but there are so many major points of difference that taxonomic confusion is excluded. When two species belong to different classes there is usually no question of homeo-morphy. Conversely the term can hardly be applied in cases where two species belong to the same genus, or to species belonging to two closely related genera where a degree of resemblance is the rule rather than the exception. Because of this Cloud only speaks of homeomorphy if the species at least belong to different subfamilies.

Homeomorphs can appear either more or less simultaneously in different branches (isochronous homeomorphy) or successively (heterochronous homeomorphy). The risk of taxonomic confusion is naturally greater in the first case. If homeomorphy is not recognised, forms may be grouped into a single species, or species into a single genus when their phylogenetic differentiation does not warrant such an arrangement. Groups formed in this way are not natural phylogenetic units, but only morphological categories. The first instances of this were described by Buckman and con-cerned brachiopods. Although examples of homeomorphy have since been discovered in nearly all the invertebrate phyla, the brachiopods have retained something of a reputation in this respect. Among the corals there are also many taxonomic puzzles caused by homeomorphy. It is probably not surprising that the phenomenon should occur so frequently in these two groups. The two groups are relatively uniform in structure, and thus the chance of homeomorphic forms is greater than in groups that have achieved a wider variation, such as the lamellibranchs.

When fairly similar forms appear in groups that are taxono-mically far apart (in different phyla or classes) the term homeo-morphy is not applicable. There is usually no further danger of taxonomic confusion in these cases, for such forms show resem-blance to each other only in some of their characters; the similarity is usually superficial, and the respective anatomical structures are essentially different. The term convergence is used in such cases. Like homeomorphy convergence is a fascinating and instructive phenomenon, because it reveals something of the connection between evolution and mode of life. However much the groups containing convergent forms may vary as a whole, the convergent forms themselves show a good deal of similarity in their mode of life. In corals, with their sessile benthonic mode of life, the cup-like form is usual. The same form, however, occurs as a rare type in groups which in general possess an entirely different shell form. In the lamellibranchs it is the rudists and in brachiopods the richthofenids which have lost some of the typical features of their own groups and evolved a cup-shaped form (Fig. 68). In certain species the individual shells even grow into a solid mass so that they form colonies in the same way as many corals. Both the rudists and the richthofenids were sessile benthonic animals. Among the vertebrates there are good examples of convergence in aquatic mammals and reptiles which, starting from two different kinds of structure, have evolved astonishingly similar types.

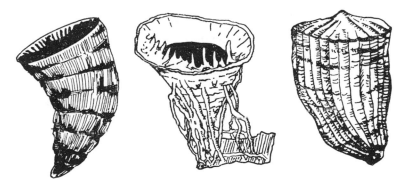

Fig. 68.   Convergence in invertebrates. From left to right a coral, a brachiopod and a lamellibranch.

Convergence and homeomorphy could be regarded as the fortuitous repetition of a type which occurs in another evolving lineage. The close connection between structural type and mode of life, however, leads most investigators to regard homeomorphy and convergence as evolutionary trends in the direction of adaptation to a particular mode of life.

It should be borne in mind that convergent tendencies in evolution remain exceptional phenomena; divergent development is much more general. Because there are such impressive examples of the latter in the vertebrates, the fact that divergent development occurs on just as large a scale in the invertebrates is liable to be forgotten. The echinoderms, the arthropods or the molluscs provide striking examples; the differences between starfish and blastoids, trilobites and butterflies, or between octopuses and rudists are not less than those between the fish and the mammals. Divergence is also strongly marked within smaller groups, especially in the gastropods, and it often continues down into the lower taxonomic units.

In Section 3 it was shown that many groups go through one and sometimes several strongly divergent phases in their evolution. Variety of forms is associated with the appearance of new ecological niches, or with the development of a new ancestral type which is potentially more adaptable than an earlier group with the same ecological niche. The term adaptive radiation is used to express this idea.

Adaptive radiation is one of the most impressive evolutionary phenomena which the palaeontologist is able to demonstrate. It is also one of the most eloquent indications of the close relationship between evolution and adaptation to ecological circumstance. It is this continual development towards better and wider ecological adaptation that many modern investigators regard as one of the most important directive factors in evolution.

The study of evolution is far from being complete at this point; adaptation should not be regarded as having functioned everywhere and at all times as the directive principle in evolution. In many cases the true significance of an observed development only emerges after very thorough analysis. A further study of the extensive subject of directional trends in evolution lies beyond the scope of this work. There is all the more inducement to forgo this discussion as various modern works, among them that of Simpson (1953), have covered this field in detail. The theme of this section will be taken up again in the next but viewed from a different angle.

6. *Biological and geological evolution*

The environment in which the processes of life are enacted is, as far as its inorganic aspects are concerned, largely the result of geological factors. If adaptation to this environment is an important directive factor in the development of life, this implies that the Earth's crustal history influences evolution. The connection between biological and geological evolution can be approached in different ways, without involving the factor of adaptation. A certain rhythm in the patterns of biological and geological development made various researchers suspect a connection long before adaptation was recognised as an important element in evolution. Much has been written by both geologists and palaeontologists on this subject which lies in the area where their respective studies meet, but the problems entailed have by no means been solved. Not only have different investigators come to different conclusions concerning the nature of the relationship, but there is not even unanimity as to whether or not it exists.

Much of the discussion centres on the question of whether there is a relationship between the evolution of life and the tectonic history of the Earth's crust, and a great deal of attention has been given to the fairly regular occurrence of phases of folding. Schindewolf (1950, Fig. 16) puts a survey of the most important peaks and turning points—it is not altogether clear how these have been selected—in the evolution of twenty of the large systematic groups alongside a time scale with the more important phases of folding. The latter are largely taken from Stille. Schindewolf is quite correct in concluding that there is no correlation between the two phenomena. Probably there is no palaeontologist who could suggest, for example, what sort of influence the Asturian phase by itself may have had on the general pattern of evolution. It would be wrong, however, to conclude from these data, as Schindewolf does, that there is no connection between geological and biological evolution. Tectonic development is undoubtedly a fundamental aspect of the evolution of the Earth's crust; it is not the only aspect, however, and palaeontologically it is not an essential one. More important is the distribution of land and sea, the development of relief and climate, etc. The evolution of life set in the framework of geological history offers a more fruitful line of study than the tectonic approach.

If there is a connection between geological and biological evolution it is reasonable to assume that particular geological events have influenced the evolutionary history of groups depending on comparable environmental conditions in a similar manner. In order to compare the evolutionary patterns of different groups, use can be made of the data referred to in Section 4 such as the total number of genera per million years and the number of new genera per million years. Fig. 69 gives the number of new genera per million years for the corals and crinoids. These two curves show a striking parallelism. There is a similar correspondence among the brachiopods, the bryozoans and the ostracods and between the foraminifers and the echinoids. Between groups belonging to different combinations, however, there are considerable differences. This is immediately apparent if the curves for the bryozoans and crinoids are compared.

These phenomena lend themselves to different interpretations. Schindewolf showed that the decline of the trilobites in the Devonian coincides with the rise of the ammonoids. He therefore rejected the idea of any connection here with geological events, because in his opinion it is inconceivable that the same events should have influenced two Devonian groups in opposite directions. On the other hand Newell pointed out that the decline of the trilobites also coincided with the rise of the fishes, in particular of the Placodermi, and that in the competition between the two groups the trilobites were the losers. Newell perceived a similar

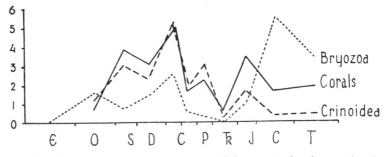

Fig. 69. Numbers of new genera per million years in the corals, the crinoids and the bryozoans. After Newell.

connection between the decline of the ammonites in the Cretaceous
and the rise of the Teleostei. Simultaneous but opposite trends in
different groups need by no means be attributed to the same
external cause, and they do not necessarily argue against a connection between geological and biological evolution.

In related groups with similar ecological requirements opposite
trends are to be expected, because such groups are to some extent
mutually exclusive. The decline of the reptiles and the simultaneous
rise of the mammals can hardly be put forward as an argument
against a connection with geological evolution. It seems much more
likely either that the development of the mammals was influenced
by a slight decline of the reptiles which increased the ecological
opportunities of the newer group, or that the decline of the reptiles
was hastened by the rise of the better adapted mammals. Fig. 70
shows similar opposite trends in other groups.

Fig. 71 gives a summary of the pattern of evolutionary trends
for 26 groups of invertebrates (classes and orders) which together

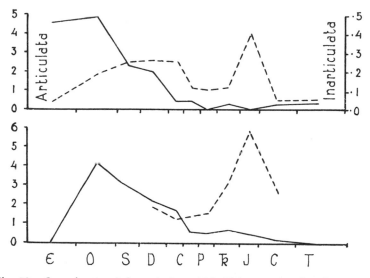

Fig. 70. Opposing trends in evolution within higher taxonomic units. *Above*:
number of new genera per million years in the articulate brachiopods (broken
line, left-hand scale) and the inarticulate brachiopods (continuous line,
right-hand scale). *Below*: number of new genera per million years in the
Nautiloidea (continuous line) and the Ammonoidea (broken line). After
Newell.

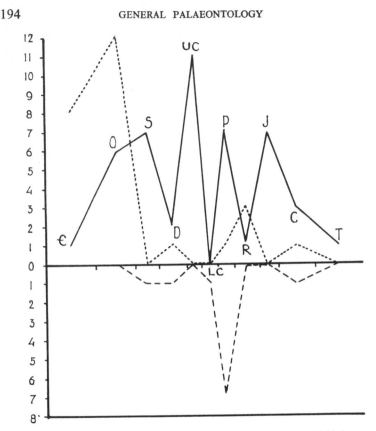

Fig. 71. Summary of a number of evolutionary trends in 26 higher taxonomic units (classes or orders). The continuous line indicates the number of
groups of new genera per million years showing maxima in the respective
periods. The dotted line gives the number of new groups (classes or orders),
the broken line the number of groups becoming extinct in the respective
period. After Newell.

include nearly the whole fauna of the shallow seas. The continuous line indicates with respect to each period the number of groups
showing peaks in their frequency curve of new genera per million
years. It is obvious that these maxima are not distributed at random
throughout geological history. There are marked accumulations in
the Ordovician and Silurian, the Lower Carboniferous, the Permian
and the Jurassic.

The curves upon which Fig. 71 is based give absolute numbers
of new genera per million years. These numbers are not repre-

sentative in that they take no account of the absolute size of a group. Ten new genera per million years in a period when a group is not very extensive represents a much more considerable development than an equal number of genera in a period in which the group has already achieved a large size. This objection is removed by relating the number of new genera to the total number of genera. Fig. 72 gives a summary of the 16 most important groups from which Fig. 71 has been assembled, but this time the curve is based on relative numbers. It now has only three maxima; those in the Ordovician and the Lower Carboniferous emerge quite clearly again, while that in the Jurassic has shifted to the Trias. This means that, in absolute terms, the number of new genera appearing in the Silurian and the Permian is high, but not in relation to the size of the groups in those periods. The shifting of the last maximum from the Jurassic to the Trias shows that in relation to the total extent of the fauna, development in the latter period exceeds that in the former.

It might be imagined that the maximum development of most invertebrates which are for the most part marine animals coincides with great world-wide transgressions. A connection between

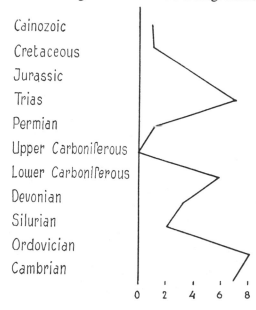

Fig. 72. The graph indicates the number of groups whose curves of the relative number of new genera (number of new genera/total number of genera) per million years shows a maximum in the period concerned. Compiled from data by Newell.

the extent of the shallow seas and the development of the marine invertebrates is not in itself inconceivable. The Triassic maximum, however, would then be difficult to understand. It comes too early, for the first great Mesozoic transgression does not occur before the beginning of the Jurassic. Newell therefore assumed that the direct influence of this geological development on the evolution of marine faunas is negative, in the sense that it is mainly the great regressions, in the transitions from the Silurian to the Devonian and the Upper Carboniferous to the Permian, that have led to the disappearance of numerous genera and various larger groups. This phenomenon is particularly marked in the Permian; it is in fact one of the most striking phenomena in the whole evolution of life.

If both major and minor taxonomic units die out the range of possible environments for the surviving groups is greatly increased. This stimulates their expansion, as new types are evolved in response to the various new conditions. As this process continues the new types in turn become part of the total environment of other groups whose ecological conditions are thereby modified. A state of relative stability is only reached after a lengthy and complicated process: after the great post-Permian expansion this was not achieved until the Jurassic. After that, decline was the only remaining possibility. The development that took place during the Cretaceous, notwithstanding a great new transgression, clearly demonstrates this.

Within the limits set by the available data—and the pitfalls referred to in Section 4 should be kept in mind—this seems to give a much more satisfactory view of the relation between geological events and the evolution of life than earlier attempts which were focused on tectonic development and which generally produced a distorted or negative picture only. The picture presented here is still crude and shows only one aspect of a complicated problem. For the sake of simplicity the invertebrate faunas have been treated as a single entity. Selection according to geographical or ecological factors might produce a further refinement and open up new points of view. A similar analysis of the evolution of terrestrial vertebrates and floras is also desirable. Simpson has attempted this for the vertebrates but produced a negative result.

It is clear that the quantitative approach to the problem represents a great step forward. The great amount of reliable taxonomic and stratigraphical information which is a primary requisite for this type of research is becoming available in increasing quantities as the large palaeontological handbooks now appearing approach their completion.

The reconnaissance that has been carried out in this section in the area between palaeontology and geology, and which has shown a possible causal connection between the development of life and that of the Earth's crust, forms a conclusion to the theme followed throughout this book: that fossils are living elements in geological evolution. This last section shows, perhaps more clearly than the others, that palaeontology is inseparably connected with geology.

BIBLIOGRAPHY

CHAPTER I

ABEL, O. (1927) *Lebensbilder aus der Tierwelt der Vorzeit.* 2nd ed. 714 pp. Jena, Fischer.
DEECKE, W. (1923) *Die Fossilisation.* 216 pp. Berlin, Borntraeger.
HUXLEY, J. (Ed.). (1940) *The new systematics.* 583 pp. Oxford Univ. Press.
MAYR, E., LINSLEY, E. G. and USINGER, R. L. (1953) *Methods and principles of systematic zoology.* 328 pp. New York, McGraw-Hill.
MÜLLER, A. H. (1951) Grundlagen der Biostratonomie. *Abh. dt. Akad. Wiss. Berl. Mat. alg. Naturw.,* Jahr 1950, Nr 3, 147 pp.
MÜLLER, A. H. (1957) *Lehrbuch der Paläozoologie.* Vol. I, *Allgemeine Grundlagen.* 344 pp. Jena, G. Fischer.
RICHTER, R. (1948) *Einführung in die zoologische Nomenklatur durch Erläuterung der internationalen Regeln.* 252 pp. Frankfurt, Kramer.
SCHÄFER, W. (1955) Fossilisations-Bedingungen der Meeressäuger und Vögel. *Senckenberg. leth.,* **36,** 1-25.
SCHÄFER, W. (1962) *Aktuo-Paläontologie nach Studien in der Nordsee.* 666 pp. Frankfurt am Main, Waldemar Kramer.
SCHENK, E. T., and MCMASTERS, J. H. (1956) *Procedure in taxonomy.* 3rd ed. by Keen, A. M. and Muller, S. W. 119 pp. Stanford Univ. Press.
SIMPSON, G. G. (1945) The principles of classification and a classification of mammals. *Bull. Am. Mus. Nat. Hist.,* **85,** 350 pp.
SIMPSON, G. G. (1961) *Principles of animal taxonomy.* 247 pp. New York and London, Columbia Univ. Press.
SYLVESTER-BRADLEY, P. C. (Ed.). (1956) *The species concept in palaeontology.* A symposium. London, The Systematics Association, Publication 2, 145 pp.
TRUEMAN, A. E. (1941) The ammonite body-chamber, with special reference to the buoyancy and mode of life of the living ammonite. *Q. J. geol. Soc., Lond.,* **96,** 339-383.
WALTHER, J. (1904) Die Fauna der Solnhofener Plattenkalke, bionomisch betrachtet. *Denkschr. med.-naturw. Ges. Jena,* **11,** 133-214.

CHAPTER II

AGER, D. V. (1963) *Principles of paleoecology.* 371 pp. New York, McGraw-Hill.
ALLEE, W. C., PARK, O., EMERSON, A. E., PARK T. and SCHMIDT, K. P. (1949) *Principles of animtl ecology.* 837 pp. Philadelphia, Saunders.
CRAIG, G. Y. (1954) The palaeoecology of the Top Hosie Shale (Lower-Carboniferous) at a locality near Kilsyth. *Q. J. geol. Soc., London,* **110,** 103-118.
ELIAS, M. K. (1937) Depth of deposition of the Big Blue (Late Paleozoic) sediments in Kansas. *Bull. geol. Soc. Am.,* **48,** 403-432.

ELLISON, Jr., S. P. (1955) Economic applications of paleoecology. *Econ. Geol.*, **50**, pt II, 867-884.

HEDBERG, H. D. (1934) Some recent and fossil brackish to fresh-water foraminifera. *J. Paleont.*, **8**, 469-476.

HEDGEPETH, J. W. (Ed.). (1957) *Ecology. Treatise on marine ecology and paleoecology*, vol. 1. Geol. Soc. Am., Memoir 67. 1296 pp.

IMBRIE, J., and NEWELL, N. (Eds.). (1964) *Approaches to paleoecology.* 432 pp. New York, John Wiley.

LADD, H. S. (Ed.). (1957) *Paleoecology. Treatise on marine ecology and paleoecology*, vol. 2. Geol. Soc. Am., Memoir 67. 1077 pp.

MOORE, R. C. (1957) Modern methods of paleoecology. *Bull. Am. Ass. Petrol. Geol.* **41**, 1775-1801.

MÜLLER, A. H. (1950) Stratonomische Untersuchungen im oberen Muschelkalk des Thüringer Beckens. *Geologica*, **4**, 74 pp.

NEWELL, N., RIGBY, J. K., FISCHER, A. G., WHITEMAN, A. J., HICKOX, J. E. and BRADLEY, J. S. (1953) *The Permian reef complex of the Guadalupe Mountains region Texas and New Mexico. A study in paleoecology.* 236 pp. San Francisco. W. H. Freeman.

SCOTT, G. (1940) Paleoecological factors controlling the distribution and mode of life of Cretaceous ammonoids in the Texas area. *J. Paleont.*, **14**, 299-323.

WASMUND, E. (1926) Biocönose und Thanatocönose. *Archs Hydrobiol.*, **17**, 1-117.

CHAPTER III

ARKELL, W. J. (1956) *Jurassic geology of the world.* 806 pp. Edinburgh, Oliver and Boyd.

BEAUFORT, L. F. DE (1926) *Zoögeographie van den Indischen Archipel.* 202 pp. Haarlem, Bohn.

BEAUFORT, L. F. DE (1943) *Zoögeographie. De verspreiding der dieren over de Aarde.* 186 pp. Noorduijn's wetenschappelijke reeks. 15 Gorinchem.

BERTSCH, K. (1940) *Geschichte des deutschen Waldes.* 120 pp. Jena, G. Fischer.

CAIN, S. A. (1944) *Foundations of plant geography.* 556 pp. New York, Harper and Bros.

DANSEREAU, P. (1957) *Biogeography, an ecological perspective.* 394 pp. New York, Ronald.

EKMAN, S. (1953) *Zoögeography of the sea.* 417 pp. London, Sedgwick and Jackson.

GERTH, H. (1925) Die Bedeutung der tertiären Riffkorallenfauna des malavischen Archipels für die Entwicklung der lebenden Riff-Fauna im indopazifischen und atlantischen Gebiet. *Verh. geol.-mijnb. Genoot. Ned.*, **8**, 173-196.

GODWIN, H. (1956) *The history of the British flora.* 384 pp. Cambridge Univ. Press.

GOOD, R. (1947) *The geography of the flowering plants.* 403 pp. London, Longmans, Green.

HESSE, R., ALLEE. W. C. and SCHMIDT, K. P. (1951) *Ecological animal geography.* 2nd ed. 715 pp. New York, Wiley.

HUPÉ, P. (1953) Classe des trilobites. In Piveteau, J., *Traité de paléontologie*, Vol. III, pp. 44-246.

JOLEAUD, L. (1923) Essai sur l'évolution des milieux géophysiques et bio-géographiques. *Bull. Soc. géol. Fr., Ser. 4*, **23**, 205-257.
JOLEAUD, L. (1939) *Atlas de paléobiogéographie.* 99 pl. Paris, Lechevalier.
KAMPEN, P. N. VAN (1929) *De geographische verspreiding der dieren (zoögeographie).* 244 pp. Amsterdam, Wereldbibliotheek.
LITZELMANN, E. (1938) Pflanzenwanderungen im Klimawechsel der Nacheiszeit. *Schr. dtsch. naturw. Ver.,* **7,** 47 pp.
SIMPSON, G. G. (1953) Evolution and geography. An essay on historical biogeography with special reference to mammals. *Condon. Lect.,* 64 pp. Oregon.
WILSON, J. L. (1957) Geography of olenid trilobite distribution and its influence on Cambro-Ordovician correlation. *Am. J. Sci.,* **255,** 321-340.

CHAPTER IV

ARKELL. W. J. (1933) *The Jurassic System in Great Britain.* 681 pp. Oxford Univ. Press.
ARKELL, W. J. (1946) Standard of the European Jurassic. *Bull. geol. Soc. Am.,* **57,** 1-34.
ARKELL. W. J. (1956) *Jurassic geology of the world.* 806 pp. Edinburgh, Oliver and Boyd.
DIENER, C. (1925) *Grundzüge der Biostratigraphie.* 304 pp. Leipzig. Deuticke.
JELETZKY, J. A. (1956) Paleontology, basis of practical geochronology. *Bull. Am. Ass. Petrol. Geol.,* **40,** 679-706.
MOORE. R. C. (1948) Stratigraphical paleontology. *Bull. geol. Soc. Am.,* **59,** 301-325.
PIA, J. (1930) *Grundbegriffe der Stratigraphie mit ausführlicher Anwendung auf die europäische Mitteltrias.* 252 pp. Leipzig, Deuticke.
SCHINDEWOLF, O. H. (1950) *Grundlagen und Methoden der paläontologischen Chronologie.* 3rd ed. 152 pp. Berlin, Borntraeger.

CHAPTER V

BRINKMANN, R. (1929) Statistisch-biostratigraphische Untersuchungen an mitteljurassischen Ammoniten über Artbegriff und Stammesentwicklung. *Abh. Ges. Wiss. Göttingen. Math.-wiss. Kl (n.F.),* **13,** 249 pp.
CLOUD, Jr., P. E. (1948) Some problems and patterns of evolution exemplified by fossil invertebrates. *Evolution,* **2,** 322-350.
HENBEST, L. G. (Ed.). (1952) Distribution of evolutionary explosions in geologic time. A symposium. *J. Paleont.,* **26,** 297-394.
KAUFMANN, R. (1933) Variationsstatistische Untersuchungen über die "Artabwandlung" und "Artumbildung" an den oberkambrischen Trilobitengattung Olenus Dalm. *Abh. geol-palaeont. Inst. Greifswald,* **10,** 1-54.
KERMACK, K. A. (1954) A biometrical study of Micraster coranguinum and M. (Isomicraster) senonensis. *Phil. Trans. R. Soc. Lond. B,* **237,** 375-428.
NICHOLS, D. (1959) Changes in the Chalk heart-urchin Micraster interpreted in relation to living forms. *Phil. Trans. R. Soc. Lond. B,* **242,** 347-437
SCHINDEWOLF, O. H. (1950) *Der Zeitfaktor in Geologie und Paläontologie.* 114 pp. Stuttgart, Schweizerbart.
SIMPSON, G. G. (1953) *The major features of evolution.* 434 pp. New York, Columbia Univ. Press.

SWINNERTON, H. H. (1941) The study of variation in fossils. *Q. J. geol. Soc. Lond.*, **96**, 77-118

UMBGROVE, J. H. F. (1946) *Leven en materie.* 3rd ed. 140 pp. 's-Gravenhage, Nijhoff.

VAUGHN, A. (1905) The paleontological sequence in the Carboniferous limestone of the Bristol area. *Q. J. geol. Soc. Lond.*, **61**, 181-305

WENGER, R. (1957): Die germanischen Ceratiten. *Palaeontographica*, **108 A,** 57-129.

WILLIAMS, A. (1957) Evolutionary rates of brachiopods. *Geol. Mag.*, **94,** 201-211.

INDEX